North Dakota's Missouri River

by Andy Mork

NORTH DAKOTA'S MISSOURI RIVER

Author - Andy Mork
Publisher - Crain Grosinger Publishing
Editor - Paula Crain Grosinger
Typesetter - Lynn C. Beck

Front cover photo: Missouri River as scene from Double Ditch Indian Village north of Bismarck, ND showing protected bank. Fifteen homes are nestled among the trees with only a few visible.

Back cover photos: Author Andy Mork; sandbars as viewed looking to the south on the Missouri River at Bismarck; erosion along Missouri River banks with loss of live cottonwoods.

International Standard Book Number: 09720054-1-2
Printed in the United States of America
by Sentinel Printing Co., Inc., St. Cloud, Minnesota

ACKNOWLEDGMENTS

FOR THEIR ASSISTANCE AND SUPPORT I WOULD
ESPECIALLY LIKE TO THANK

My wife, Grace

The North Dakota Water Coalition

The North Dakota State Historical Society

Engineering Staff of the
North Dakota Water Commision

North Dakota Water Users Association

Michael Dwyer

Andrea Collin

Angela Magstadt

Ron Sando

The U.S. Geological Survey

North Dakota Living Magazine

PHOTOS PROVIDED BY

Andy Mork

Paula Crain Grosinger

Throndset Studios, Bismarck

North Dakota Water Education Foundation

*"Out West, God provided plenty of whiskey to drink,
and just enough water to fight over."*
-Samuel Clemens

*"No water falling within these upper basin states
should flow beyond their boundaries."*
-John Wesley Powell
Director of the U.S. Geological Survey urging
development of irrigation in the
Dakotas and Montana

Foreword

What is the difference between good stewardship and ideological arrogance? The various viewpoints regarding water resource management have raised this question repeatedly. Nowhere is the issue more prominent than on the Missouri River, specifically the northern reaches of the Missouri River.

Disagreements and battles over water are nothing new in the Dakotas. Agrarian Native American tribes, such as the Mandan and Arikara, depended on the river and the deposition of fertile soil that followed the usually turgid spring flows. Even the nomadic plains hunters knew the importance of protecting water rights. While they had a generally fluid concept of land ownership, these tribes asserted water rights over other tribes and the advancing European settlers. Their approach was simple – whoever used the water had the right to it.

There is a great divide between water law east of the Mississippi and west of the Mississippi. In the east, the European philosophy of riparian rights prevailed. This view holds that water and its boundary land are inseparable in perpetuity. Those who own the land bordering a river, stream or body of water have exclusive rights to the resource whether or not they use it. An upstream landowner, however, may not divert or block the water from those downstream.

As the white man moved west, another concept of water rights evolved apart from the eastern riparian view. In 1819, fifteen years after Lewis & Clark started upstream, the first steamboat navigated the Missouri River as far as Council Bluffs, Iowa. The federal government, which already asserted authority over navigable waterways, sought to extend its authority to the tributaries that fed into these waterways. In 1824, Congress authorized the U.S. Army Corps of Engineers (the Corps) to aid navigation. In 1838, the Corps undertook "snagging" efforts to facilitate Missouri River navigation.

In the 1860s, lands west of the Mississippi became available under the Homestead Act and the great migration of white settlers began in earnest. In 1866, Congress enacted legislation setting the tone for western water law. The new law recognized mining, agriculture, and manufacturing interests and specifically addressed the concept of water rights based on prior use of Missouri basin water. Indian claims to water aside, those using the water for what was considered a beneficial purpose were considered to have vested rights to the resource.

Completion of the first transcontinental railroad through the Missouri River basin in 1869 and the Colorado gold rush in 1876 solidified the western doctrine of appropriation. The concept held that the first user on a stream has priority rights to the stream, the next user has second priority, and so on, providing that the water is put to a beneficial use. While there were many early western water wars over who owns the water, in later years the battles have been largely between states and the federal government over who has priority in making the best use of the resource. As environmentalists entered the debate the "beneficial use" concept has also been interpreted to include applications that do not directly serve human needs.

So, water resource management and the management of the Missouri River have become a very complex issue with a host of entities trying to expound what is, in their view, the best way to manage both the water, the waterway, and the riparian land.

Perhaps only time will tell if we have been good stewards of the river. One thing is certain: the construction of dams on the upper reaches and the channelizing of the lower river have changed forever the course, the dynamics and the essence of the Missouri River. Large urban centers along the river have avoided major flooding for most of the last fifty years. Good quality water has been made available to semi-arid areas of the country. New uses for the river and surrounding valley have been and are being discovered.

In the early years of the 21st century, the river has been the subject of intense legal debate with small upstream states trying to defend their interests against the political clout of downstream states which have the support of the Corps of Engineers. Upstream, the goal has been to reduce river flows to maintain water levels for irrigation, recreation and the preservation of endangered species. Downstream states argue for higher releases in order to maintain their limited barge shipping enterprises. Ironically, while the river is essentially channelized by concrete and other means downstream, upstream riparian landowners have found themselves at odds with the Corps and environmentalists when they have wanted to make property improvements to stabilize their banks. In spite of all this acrimony, we have largely avoided buying and selling Missouri River water as a commodity. But just as the river continues its flow, the battle over how best to manage the river continues.

It is sad to think the river's modern legacy could be that of unresolved conflict, especially when there are those who have a crisp vision of the river's potential. Andy Mork is one of those visionaries. He has lived the better part of a century on North Dakota's Missouri River.

What follows is derived from Mr. Mork's experience, his in-depth knowledge of the river, and his belief in the potential of this resource. Mork is a learned man with a degree in engineering and a long record of conservation and water resource management expertise. Without imposing intellectual hubris upon the reader, *"North Dakota's Missouri River"* is a primer for good stewardship for anyone living in the upper Missouri River region.

Table of Contents

To my wife, Grace.

Preface

My love affair and appreciation of our river goes back to at least 1926, when I was a five-year-old boy. I sat on the banks and watched the last paddlewheel boat operate on the river. The railroad had arrived in Bismarck in 1872, which eliminated the need for riverboats to ship the heavy freight; rail branch lines were built in 1910 north to Stanton and south to Cannon Ball, but there was still need for the boats to supply the need for the areas farther north and south. They carried considerable wheat (handled in two-bushel bags) to Bismarck where it was shipped by rail east to market.

In 1926, the boats had been converted with large gas engine motors, eliminating the need for the wood yards along the rivers and the troublesome steam boilers. The boats were pulled out of the river over winter at a government owned facility called Rock Haven (because of natural rock protected banks there) three miles north of Mandan. I had an opportunity to explore the boats there where they were stored until their service was discontinued and they were sold for salvage. They remain, for me, an important connection with the river's history.

Our family moved into the high river bottom eight miles north of Mandan in 1931 and established the Mork farm. We had many neighbors then, all of us attracted by the rich level bottomland soil and the water in the river. Primitive irrigation at least provided us with lush gardens and the wood provided us with heat. We were well-fed and warm, even in the desperate drought and depression years of the 1930s.

I grew up enjoying the four seasons of the river. Boating and swimming in the summer and skating and exploring the islands across the ice in the winter. An occasional catfish furnished a great meal! We were naively unaware of the flood danger since there had been no floods in the recent past and none during the drought years. We had no Water Commission or Corps of Engineers active then to warn us of the danger. However, a flood in 1939 brought two feet of water over our land and alerted the valley residents of the potential danger.

This valley has always been home to me, even during my college years and the few years it took me to know I could never have a love affair with the likes of Chicago, New York, and Minneapolis! The Missouri Flood Control Act of 1944 authorized the dams on the Missouri and the flood control it would provide to our reach of the river. I came back in 1945, married and built our home at the Mork farm. We crossed our fingers and hoped it would not flood until the Garrison Dam was closed, but as you will learn, the Missouri needed one more binge before it would surrender to the dams!

Because of my long and intense relationship with the river, both before and after the dams, I have of necessity and my compelling interest, achieved a broad knowledge of all aspects of our river. I trust my engineering capacities and the facts I have compiled will give a realistic view of our valley and its many problems and potentials.

With this background it seemed desirable that I publish my knowledge and recommendations for the consideration of present and future river valley users. I hope it will be of value to you. It doesn't take a person with a doctorate degree in mathematics to know what two and two are. In like manner, one doesn't need a degree in many other areas to come to valid conclusions. A few simple facts and common sense help one arrive at the conclusions and recommendations herein, and I accept full responsibility for them. The source of the facts published is identified in the text.

You will notice considerable repetition of many of the facts about our river, but hopefully this redundancy will add to your appreciation and understanding of our precious valley.

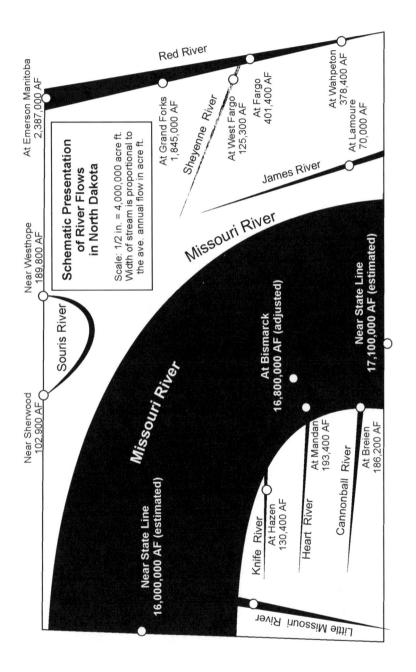

**Schematic Presentation
of River Flows
in North Dakota**

Scale: 1/2 in. = 4,000,000 acre ft.
Width of stream is proportional to
the ave. annual flow in acre ft.

Red River

At Emerson Manitoba
2,387,000 AF

At Grand Forks
1,845,000 AF

Sheyenne River

At West Fargo
125,300 AF

At Fargo
401,400 AF

At Wahpeton
378,400 AF

At Lamoure
70,000 AF

James River

Missouri River

Near Westhope
189,800 AF

Souris River

Near Sherwood
102,900 AF

Missouri River

At Bismarck
16,800,000 AF (adjusted)

Near State Line
17,100,000 AF (estimated)

At Mandan
193,400 AF

Heart River

At Hazen
130,400 AF

Knife River

Cannonball River

At Breien
186,200 AF

Near State Line
16,000,000 AF (estimated)

Little Missouri River

1

THE WAY IT WAS

If we are to understand and appreciate our Missouri River with its Garrison and Oahe Dams, the lakes they have created, and the free flowing reaches, we must first remember the river the way it was.

Geologists inform us that instead of flowing south through North Dakota, the Missouri River formerly flowed east and then exited north into the Hudson Bay drainage. With ice extending southward over about two-thirds of North Dakota during the last glacier era, the river was forced to find a new channel southward and so its present route was determined. About 10,000 years ago during the warming years at the end of the glacier era, a huge amount of water flowed from the melting ice and the Missouri River became an enormous body of moving water. It extended between the present day bluffs and was 100 to 200 feet deep in North Dakota. Contemporary well drillers verify this by finding the same river silt soils down to those depths and also by bringing up wood chips from trees deposited by the receding ice and its melt thousands of years ago.

As the glacier diminished and the flows reduced, the river no longer needed this large and deep channel. It gradually filled the excess channel with soil eroded from its tributaries. Thus, the river that Lewis & Clark found, and as we knew until the dams were built, was developed.

The Missouri River drains all of Montana east of the Rocky Mountains, the northern two-thirds of Wyoming and even a small area of Canada. It would have been a much larger river if this vast area were not a low precipitation region.

The old Missouri River began each new year flowing peacefully under a thickening ice cap. At this northern latitude during the winter there was no rain or snowmelt to augment the river flow, so the river was at a low four to five foot river stage (see Appendix 1). The ice could become three to five feet thick depending on the thickness of the insulating snow cover and the severity of the winter temperatures. This thick river ice became an important transportation route for crossings and provided a level north-south road. Visits between families across the river were eagerly anticipated events of the winter season. The strong ice permitted several winter sports such as skating, ice fishing and ice sailing. The Northern Pacific Railway Company laid tracks on the ice to transport material across the river before and during the building of their railway bridge at Bismarck. This bridge was completed in 1875.

In spring, local and eastern Montana snowmelt brought a sudden surge of water into North Dakota and along with the melt came the potential for ice-jam flooding.

The ice-jam floods on the pre-dam Missouri River in North Dakota were an awesome spectacle. They were somewhat predictable and only occurred about every 20 years. They came and went quickly, usually within a week or less, but all who lived along or had property on the river were very concerned until the "river went out" each spring. With the promise of flood control after the anticipated closing of the Garrison Dam in late

1953, considerable permanent building began in the late 1940s. Each spring these owners hoped they could escape a damaging flood until the dam was closed. But the Missouri River had a mind of its own and had "one last fling" before it was shackled behind a dam. The river delivered a near record ice-jam flood in the spring of 1952.

All the conditions required for ice-jam flooding were present that spring. The river in North Dakota had flowed somewhat higher than average during the winter, there was little insulating snow cover on the ice, and winter temperatures were colder than normal. This resulted in a wide ice cover that measured four to five feet thick. The Yellowstone and Missouri watershed in eastern Montana experienced much above-normal snowfall. The spring thaws in Montana, which normally are much earlier than in North Dakota, delivered above-normal water into North Dakota when the huge ice cover was still rigid. The whole ice sheet floated up and began moving downstream, but couldn't go far and became a huge ice dam. Water levels rose quickly behind the ice, flooding the adjacent high bottomland (see Appendix 2). The increasing water levels eventually floated the ice dam downstream where the whole process was repeated again and again down the Missouri River until it reached thinner ice farther south usually in central or southern South Dakota.

When the ice dam just above Bismarck broke, the river reached a high stage of 24.7 feet and flowed at 500,000 cubic feet per second. Compare that with river stages now of six to 13 feet and average flows of 22,000 cfs! Water depths of six to 10 feet were common on the high bottomland. This flood was predictable so livestock and other moveable property could be protected. Thankfully, there was no loss of human life, but there were large wildlife and other losses. Where the ice dams and the large water flows moved, many deer on ice cakes, hay stacks, buildings and other debris floated downstream. Buildings that were protected by trees were protected from damaging ice flows, but all other property was destroyed.

With the restricting ice cover gone, the river quickly returned to its channel. Traffic on the high bottomland returned to normal in less than a week! The Garrison Dam was closed in late 1953 and the threat of ice-jam floods was gone forever. Permanent development along the Garrison to Oahe reach began.

After the "ice went out" the river returned to a low river stage until the snowmelt of western Montana and northern Wyoming arrived. This "June rise" usually came in late May and lasted until early August. The June rise reached a stage of 10 to 12 feet, but did not flood the high bottomland. An exception occurred in 1997 when a 200-year June rise event occurred which would have covered all high bottomland with water four to six feet deep (see graph). The Garrison Dam prevented any flooding by controlling discharges and thus verifying that the Garrison to Oahe Reach is no longer considered a flood plain.

The June rise covered most low sandbars and pre- vented the growth of any vegetation during the warm summer months. Flooding these bare sandbars also prevented the nesting of shore birds such as terns and plovers during their nesting periods. By flooding other sandbars that were vegetated it also discouraged the nesting of geese, ducks and other waterfowl. An ex- ception here was the extreme drought years when the June rise was very low and the nesting habitat was avail- able. Lewis and Clark did observe shore birds and waterfowl on their trip through North Dakota, but they

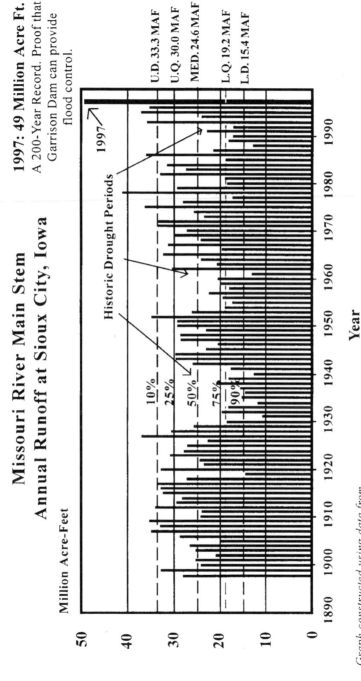

Missouri River Main Stem
Annual Runoff at Sioux City, Iowa

1997: 49 Million Acre Ft.
A 200-Year Record. Proof that
Garrison Dam can provide
flood control.

Million Acre-Feet

U.D. 33.3 MAF
U.Q. 30.0 MAF
MED. 24.6 MAF
L.Q. 19.2 MAF
L.D. 15.4 MAF

1997

Historic Drought Periods

10%
25%
50%
75%
90%

50

40

30

20

10

0

1890 1900 1910 1920 1930 1940 1950 1960 1970 1980 1990

Year

Graph constructed using data from
U.S. Geological Survey and U.S. Army Corps of Engineers

5

came here in the fall when these birds were obviously gathering from all areas in preparation for their migration.

The June rise, flowing deep and swift, carried heavy loads of sediment. As it traversed the vegetated sandbars it was retarded and deposited soil. Thus began the building of the high bottomland. Obviously, the June rise could only aggrade the sandbars up to its maximum level which was about a 10 to 12-foot river stage. The remaining building of the high bottomland, which is higher than a 13-foot river stage, had to wait for the occasional ice-jam floods.

After completion of the mountain snowmelt the river reverted to low levels which exposed many bare sandbars. This low level continued through the fall and into the winter. The bare sandbars were exposed to the wind, and huge dust storms were common during these months. Sand-drifts (like snowdrifts) were formed where the sand-laden wind was slowed by trees. Soil classifiers have noted a difference in the soils miles away from the river because of the river dust storms.

As it traversed the plains, the Missouri River was (except for its increasing size and decreasing slope as it flowed south) very similar in Montana, North Dakota, South Dakota, Nebraska, Iowa and Missouri. Being an alluvial river, it carried a heavy silt load and was constantly eroding and rebuilding its adjacent high bottomlands. The bank erosion occurred on the outside of the river channel curves where the velocity and the centrifugal force of the water was greatest. The rebuilding began on the inside of the curves where the current was slower. Thus, the river's curves slowly migrated downstream.

The building of the high bottomland required floods like the 1952 event to transport sediment onto the land. It is interesting how much sediment was deposited by this typical flood. In investigating the 4,000 acre Square Butte area, the deposition varied from as much as one foot in extremely small areas downstream from a heavily wooded area, to one-fourth inch in most other areas. The average was less than one-half inch. Floods of this magnitude occurred only about once in 20 years. The conclusion here is that the process of rebuilding the high bottomland we now know was very slow. The evidence, including the age of some trees and the carbon dating of bark and wood deposited in the 12 to 15-foot levels, indicates the average high bottomlands are hundreds to thousands of years old.

The old Missouri River, with its hundreds of miles of eroding banks and sandbars in various stages of re-building, was cluttered with tree trunks deposited anywhere and everywhere. This made navigation very difficult and dangerous. Many early paddle wheels were

The author enjoyed bathing in "Old Muddy" in the 1930s & 1940s. He is pictured back row, far right. While full of sediment, the river was clean and relatively free of contaminants.

damaged or sunk by hitting these snags. The government attempted to clear these snags with its boats, but the task was almost impossible. If the river had not been changed by the dams and the bank protection we now have, pleasure boating as we know it would be dangerous and undesirable.

The plants, fish, birds and other animals indigenous to the "Old Muddy" were those that could live with the turbid water and the other characteristics of this stream. Catfish, bullheads, carp, sturgeon, garfish, ling and other bottom feeders made up the fishery. Those fish that depend on sight to feed could not exist here. The river was a great spring and fall migratory route for all waterfowl and countless other bird species. However, since the June rise covered all sandbars from late May to early August (except for extreme drought years), plovers, terns, ducks, geese and other shore nesting birds were unable to nest here.

At the time of Lewis and Clark the animals here included grizzly and black bears, wolves, buffalo and elk. These are no longer naturally present, but deer, antelope, coyotes, badgers, beavers, porcupines, rabbits, fox, squirrels and numerous other species have continued to exist. The introduction of pheasants in 1930 added to the upland bird species of grouse and partridges. Bald eagles, hawks and many other migratory birds were and still are present.

Cottonwood trees were natural to the old Missouri River conditions. They sprouted on the low sandbars, could tolerate considerable water during the June rise, and remained as the sandbars grew vertically to become huge trees on the high bottomland. Their enemies were natural or set fires, or the river itself that sometimes eroded them into the river. The cottonwood was also a favorite food of the beaver. They destroyed many prime groves. The ash, box elder and oak were less tolerant of water, but grew easily on the high bottomland when it was established. The sandbar willow, whose seed seemed to be everywhere, grew the instant the sandbars were out of water during the warm months, and began to trap water borne sediment and thus started the building of higher sandbars and, eventually, high bottomland.

This was the river that Lewis and Clark found when they made their epic journey through North Dakota on their way to and from the Pacific Ocean. It was the same river that had existed in the thousands of years since the melting of the last glacier and the same river that existed until the installation of the Pick-Sloan dams. It carried silt which had eroded from its huge watershed and from its banks. It redeposited enough sediment to rebuild as much high bottomland as it had eroded so the total amount of high bottomland remained constant. The excess sediment load continued downstream and eventually was added to the Mississippi delta.

2

THE GREAT TRANSITION

The pre-dam Missouri River plagued North Dakota, Montana and South Dakota periodically with ice-jam floods. Farther south, where the winter ice was thinner, ice-jam flooding was less of a problem. However, the river delivered the snow melt water from western Montana and northern Wyoming into the lower states of Nebraska, Iowa, Kansas and Missouri at a time that coincided with their summer rainy season. If the snowmelt was large and the local rains were above normal, disastrous flooding resulted. These heavy flows also affected the Mississippi River by adding to its flood levels.

The lower Missouri River floods not only affected the broad high bottomlands, but also many riverside cities. In 1943, three separate flood crests in March, May and June inundated much of the riparian land along the lower Missouri River, including Kansas City and Omaha. The rampaging Missouri River demanded attention!

The civilian branch of the U. S. Army Corps of Engineers, which has existed since 1794, had been studying the Missouri and Mississippi Rivers for years. The Corps had a long history of building and improving harbors, improving navigation on rivers and building flood control dams throughout the nation. Beginning in the late 1800s it had built 600 dams in 60 years.

The Corps' plan for the Missouri River was to build several large dams in North Dakota and South Dakota to provide storage for floodwater and to develop hydropower. Its plan also included channelizing the lower river from Sioux City to St. Louis for navigation. The dams would provide water for summer navigation, and the hydropower would help pay for the project. The plan also included levees along the lower river as needed.

At the same time, the Bureau of Reclamation (which also had a long history of building dams in the west with the focus of providing water and hydropower for irrigation) was studying the Missouri River. The Bureau plan called for dams on the upper river and its tributaries to provide flood control, and water and power for irrigation. They had no plans for lower river navigation.

Both entities, with their various supporters, were requesting Congressional approval for their plans. Although the devastating floods of 1943 brought urgency to the problem, neither side would agree to change or withdraw their plan.

This impasse resulted in another plan by the affected states. They proposed a Missouri Valley Authority that would be copied after the Tennessee Valley Authority (TVA). The TVA was governed by a board appointed by the federal government and was not tied to the Corps of Engineers or the Bureau of Reclamation. Since the Corps and the Bureau could not seem to agree on any plan, the Missouri Valley Authority's plan could succeed. Col. Lewis Pick of the Corps and Glenn Sloan of the Bureau of Reclamation quickly resolved their differences and proposed a joint plan to Congress.

The new plan included the navigation channel, the levees, the large dams, smaller upstream dams and irrigation development. The Corps would build and operate the dams, the navigation channel and the hydropower plants. The Bureau of Reclamation would market the power produced and develop and administer the irrigation systems. The plan, known as the Flood Control Act of 1944, passed Congress, and with some amendments since, is the law that governs what we now call the Pick-Sloan Project.

The Pick-Sloan Project included the Fort Peck Dam on the Missouri River in east central Montana, which had been completed in 1940, the Garrison Dam in North Dakota, the Oahe, Ft. Randall, Big Bend and Gavins Point dams in South Dakota. The project included several dams on the upper tributaries of the Missouri River and irrigation development in Montana, North Dakota and South Dakota. Also included was the channelizing of the river from Sioux City to St. Louis to provide river navigation for this reach. The channelization consisted of rock revetment on both sides of the river to confine the river into a narrow and deep channel. Several oxbow curves were eliminated thereby shortening the river by over 125 miles.

This channel improvement cost $750,000 per mile in 1950 dollars and was justified by allocating 75 percent of the cost to adjacent land improvement (eliminating bank erosion) and 25 percent to navigation benefits (see Appendix 9). The channel improvement and its perpetual maintenance were part of the Pick-Sloan Project cost.

The chain of Pick-Sloan dams in North Dakota and South Dakota, while greatly reducing the flood crests on the lower river, did not provide complete flood control of local rivers in that area of large average rainfall. Therefore, to provide flood control to the lands adjacent to the lower Missouri River, hundreds of miles of levees were built together with the pumps necessary to evacuate the water behind the levees during high river levels. These levees also were built at federal expense. After World War II was concluded in 1945, construction of the project moved forward rapidly.

The Garrison Dam was closed in 1953 and reached full operating levels in the early 1960s. The downstream dams were completed soon afterward.

The original plan for the Garrison Dam was for a maximum height of 1,830 feet above sea level. However, this was changed to 1,850 feet over strong objections from the city of Williston, North Dakota. Williston feared the higher elevation would deposit a delta created by the combined sediment loads of the proximate Yellowstone River and upper Missouri River. The 1,820- foot elevation of the Oahe Dam would back water to south Bismarck and the Ft. Randall Dam would back water to south Pierre. Although deltas and their negative effects were predictable in the upper reaches of all the Pick-Sloan dams, no plans for addressing these problems were included in the Pick-Sloan Project.

North Dakota gave up 550,000 acres of land to the Garrison and Oahe dams and lakes. This was an especially painful loss to the ranchers and the Indian Tribes who used the bottomlands and wooded areas for feed and shelter for their cattle. However, North Dakota was to receive development of 1.25 million acres of irrigated land complete with water delivery to that acreage. The state would receive economical power for their rapidly growing rural electric cooperatives. Also, the 80 miles of bottomland remaining between the Garrison Dam and Oahe Dam were now flood-proof and could be intensely developed for irrigation, commercial and residential use.

Environmental laws and restrictions were few or

nonexistent at the time the Pick-Sloan Project was planned and constructed. The government had eminent domain to purchase land and rights. The project was very popular with most North Dakotans, except those who lost land, so little opposition was voiced. The landowners sold out for appraised value and moved on. The Indians, whose reservation was bisected and reduced, were paid the appraised price and moving costs, but hindsight reveals that in most cases this was inadequate.

The Pick-Sloan Project, which cost $1.3 billion, consisted of many items including the construction of the dams, power plants, the navigation channel and the irrigation supply channels, land acquisition, and the removal and replacement of roads, bridges and towns. The project costs were allocated to flood control, irrigation, navigation and hydropower production. Hydropower, the only revenue producing part of the project, was required to pay back its costs during the life of the project, the remaining costs of the project were borne entirely by federal appropriation. Although recreation was recognized as an important part of the Pick-Sloan Project, it was not considered a justifiable part of the project at that time.

The Corps developed a Master Manual for the operation of the several dams during the anticipated extreme drought to extreme wet years. The objective was to maximize benefits to flood control, hydropower, navigation and irrigation. The endangered species laws had not yet been enacted and recreation, including fishing, was not considered a justifiable part of the Pick-Sloan Project, so provisions for these interests were not included in the Master Manual.

A prestigious group of engineers such as the Corps must have realized there would be some negative effects caused by the project. However, no provision was included in the project for coping with the deltas that would develop in the upper reaches of the newly created lakes, and there was no recognition of the net loss of high bottomland that would result from increased bank erosion along the remaining free flowing reaches. Obviously, the Corps decided to cope with these problems when they occurred rather then place additional financial load on the front end of the Pick-Sloan Project.

The installation of the Pick-Sloan Project on the mighty Missouri River was certainly the greatest engineered transformation any river in the world had ever undergone.

In the late 1940s and early 1950s the Mork family and others who lived on the high bottomland downstream from the Garrison Dam anxiously awaited the completion of the dam and the flood control it would provide. An annual trip to the dam site to examine the construction progress was customary.

One year we received permission to cross the river there on a temporary bridge constructed by the builders. The bridge was used to allow trucks to dump hundreds of loads of rock into the river to begin the final dam closure. I understand this bridge was left in the bottom of the dam.

One of the most memorable moments of my river watching was in the summer of 1953. We drove up to see the newly dammed river. As we drove over the divide and looked down into the valley we could see the beginning Lake Sakakawea still less than five miles long. Instead of the tan-brown of the "Old Muddy", the sediment had settled and the lake was now a beautiful blue! One has to know the "Old Muddy" like it was to appreciate the beautiful clear blue water we now have.

Another memorable occasion happened a few years later when we caught and feasted on walleye for the

15

Irrigation has turned arid upper Missouri River basin land into productive farmland making 200-bushel corn, 50-bushel soybeans, 6-ton alfalfa and 25-ton corn silage yields per acre possible.

first time. A great improvement compared to the carp, bullheads and even the catfish of the "Old Muddy".

This was only the beginning of the great transition. The flood-proofed valley began to develop in ways that had never before been possible. South Bismarck sprouted shopping centers, hotels, and numerous businesses. Farther south, hundreds of new and pretentious homes were built and the expansion continues. The "strip" in southeast Mandan developed into a huge business area and more homes were constructed south of it along the river.

The valley north of Bismarck-Mandan also responded to the new flood protection. Many riverside homes were built along the river where the banks were protected. More homes continue to be built.

Much of the land was cleared of forest and developed into prime farmland. Irrigation has been added making 200-bushel corn, 50-bushel soybeans, 6-ton alfalfa and 25-ton corn silage yields per acre now possible.

All this was possible because of the flood prevention provided by the Garrison Dam. Additional assurance was added in the summer of 1997 when the Garrison Dam successfully retained a once in 200 years June rise that otherwise would have put an estimated four feet of water in the Kirkwood shopping area and all other high bottom land of this reach.

Those are reasons why I consider our river (except for the dangerous Bismarck delta) the most improved river in the United States.

Harvesting corn silage on the Mork farm.

3

THOSE DELTAS

Almost 300 years ago the European explorers discovered the Mississippi River and traveled upstream to the first high ground. They established a city there, which we now call New Orleans. The Mississippi, like any flowing body of water, carried a load of sediment, which was deposited when the river reached the still water of the ocean. This deposition is known as a delta and is present where all sediment-laden flowing water reaches still water. As the delta increases, the upstream water levels must rise to allow the water to flow over the deposition. The deltas lengthen and broaden continually. The Mississippi delta, built over the eons of time, is now over 10,000 square miles, and continues to build.

The river at New Orleans has continued to rise and is now several feet higher than the level of the city. To prevent the flooding of the city by the rising Mississippi, levees were constructed around the entire city. Every drop of rain that falls in New Orleans must be pumped up to the river to prevent the city flooding. It is strange to drive on the streets near the levees and look up to ocean liners traveling by on a level higher than you are!

The U.S. Army Corps of Engineers, designers and builders of the Pick-Sloan Project on the Missouri River, created several lakes upstream from their dams. All had tributaries and/or upstream reaches that contributed to the sediment that began the formation of deltas in the upper reaches of the lakes.

The town of Niobrara, Nebraska was the first location to become critically affected. It was located near the confluence of the Niobrara River and the Lewis and Clark Lake upstream from the Gavins Point Dam at Yankton, South Dakota. The Niobrara River, flowing eastward across northern Nebraska, carried a heavy sediment load. The delta created there raised the bottom of the Niobrara River 15 feet and raised the ground water table in the town. This made the entire town uninhabitable. It also increased the probability and severity of flooding. This condition became critical in 1970 only 12 years after Lewis and Clark Lake was created.

Beginning in 1971, the Corps studied the problem, and recommended the entire removal of the town to higher ground. The building of dikes around the town and installing pumps or the dredging of the delta was not deemed practical.

The town population of 500, was moved in 1974 at a cost of over $11 million. The adjacent Niobrara State Park, which also was affected by the delta formation, was closed and purchased for $530,000. These costs were charged to the Pick-Sloan Project.

The Williston, North Dakota area was next to be critically affected by delta formation and subsequent high groundwater levels. Here, the Fort Peck to Lake Sakakawea reach of the Missouri and the uncontrolled Yellowstone River (which carries a heavy sediment load) empty into the Missouri River upstream from Williston. The Buford-Trenton Irrigation Project, upstream from

Williston. The Buford-Trenton Irrigation Project, upstream from Williston, was declared unusable by its board of directors in 1973. They requested the sale of their irrigation system and their flowage rights, but desired to keep the land and continue to farm if possible. The sale of the irrigation rights and some small tracts in the area was accomplished. The owners of the property were compensated, but the annual income from irrigation has been lost forever.

The water pumping plant intake for Williston has also been impacted by the delta which has raised the bottom of the river by over 17 feet. The city continues to move and attempt to improve its water intake to cope with the increasing delta. The higher water levels downstream resulted in a large swamp making Williston the unenviable mosquito capitol of the state!

Pierre, South Dakota is located just downstream from the Oahe Dam and at the upper end of Lake Sharpe, which was created by the Big Bend Dam on the Missouri. The Bad River, again carrying a heavy silt load flows into Lake Sharp downstream from Pierre. The resulting delta has made much of south Pierre uninhabitable. Again after studies, the Corps requested $35 million to buy out much of south Pierre. Fifty homes have been purchased so far, and 150 more homes and some businesses will have to be purchased. The $35 million will not be sufficient and South Dakota's Senator Daschle is requesting more funds.

The next delta, and potentially the most expensive, is building in south Bismarck/Mandan, North Dakota at the upper end of Lake Oahe. According to a U.S. Geological Survey study made in 1999, over 90 percent of the sediment load here comes from the banks and the bottom of the Garrison to Oahe reach of the Missouri River itself and less than 10 percent from the Knife

River, Heart River and other tributaries.

Compared to Niobrara, Williston and Pierre, the sediment load is much smaller due to the relatively smaller source. Also, since the level of Lake Oahe varies much more than the lakes at Niobrara and Pierre, the delta below Bismarck is distributed over several miles and thus the water levels here are rising slower than the other locations. However, unless the sediment load at Bismarck is stopped or greatly reduced, the end result will be the same.

A 1999 FEMA restudy of the Bismarck/Mandan area has raised the predicted 100-year flood level up to one foot. This will result in a major increase in flood insurance for a large affected area. And could eventually require a buy-out if the delta continues to increase. A buy-out here would cost hundreds of million of dollars!

Since winter hydropower is most profitable, the Garrison Dam power plant always attempts to produce as much power as possible then. However, the increasing delta in the Oahe headwaters has forced the Corps to reduce Garrison's winter discharge under ice from 33,000 cubic feet per second 20 years ago to 22,000 cubic feet per second now. As the delta increases more reduction of winter discharges is inevitable. Again, more financial losses due to the delta.

The delta decreases the storage capacity of Lake Oahe and results in reduced hydropower and flood storage benefits. This delta also greatly increases the probability of ice-jam flooding during both the late fall freeze and the spring breakup.

In this area, pleasure boating numbers are high. The Oahe delta is causing considerable problems, especially during low river levels. The National Walleye Fishing Tournament, which has been held at Bismarck, is becoming less attractive. Unless river flows are high, the delta makes it difficult to launch and navigate the river at Bismarck and the fishing is being forced farther down stream each year. This situation will become worse.

The solution to the Oahe delta problem will not be easy and will be very expensive. As was indicated by the Niobrara study, dredging to remove the delta or levies with pumps like at New Orleans would not be practical and also would be extremely expensive. Buying out south Bismarck-Mandan and allowing the delta to increase is also another option, but again this would cost many, many millions and cause great disruption to the community. Another possibility is the reduction of the operating level of Lake Oahe, which would move the new delta formation downstream and prevent the increase of the present delta. This option may be the only one left, but again would be expensive in the lost hydropower revenues and greatly reduced flood control and hydropower storage in the Oahe reservoir.

Therefore, it seems obvious that preventing or reducing the building of the Oahe delta is not only logical but extremely urgent. Since upstream bank and bottom erosion is over 90 percent responsible for the delta formation, this is where we should concentrate out efforts. Corps records indicate bottom degradation was rapid near Garrison Dam in the first years of the project, but has decreased due to the self-armoring effect of boulders and heavy soils embedded in the river bottom. Records show the river bottom levels of the south half of the Garrison to Oahe reach are stable, or stable to accreting. Therefore most of the sediment load must be coming from the erosion of the banks.

The 1997 report No. 576 by the North Dakota Water Commission stated that 30 percent of the total 170 miles of the banks of the Garrison to Oahe reach are already rip-rapped and are not eroding. Another 60 percent of the banks are on the inside of the river curves, are naturally rip-rapped bluffs, or do not need protection. That means only 10 percent more of the banks need protection. The cost of this 10 percent is estimated to be $13.8 million. With all the evidence of the other deltas and their problems, and the obvious increase in the Oahe delta, it is logical and very urgent that the remaining bank erosion sites be protected.

Hindsight tells us the Corps erred in its design of the Pick- Sloan Project. Obviously, the dams were too high and backed still water too near Niobrara, Williston, Pierre and Bismarck. The design achieved more hydropower, more flood protection, and more water storage, but it moved the delta-forming area too near these cities resulting in the problems we now have. The dam levels should have been reduced or, in the Bismarck area, all of the bottomland south of Bismarck/Mandan should have been purchased.

The Corps is not proactive, but rather reacts to the problems they have created only when they are forced by those affected. If they had been proactive they would have insisted on installing bank protection on the Garrison to Oahe reach when the Garrison Dam was built. As engineers, the Corps should have included bank protection as an integral part of the Pick-Sloan Project since delta formation and their problems are elementary!

The issue of the Oahe delta is not whether it will cause increasing problems, but when. It must be dealt with now. With the Niobrara, Pierre and Williston examples, it is obvious that any more delay is intolerable and unconscionable. It is also discouraging that the owners in the delta area are not more proactive in demanding that the Corps protect their land. They are either uninformed or do not wish to have their problems exposed for fear of a reduction of home and land values.

Our state engineer and state government must give this problem a priority equal to the flood problems at Grand Forks, Fargo and Devils Lake before it is too late.

Dredging on the Missouri River near the Heskett Station power plant intake north of Mandan in the fall of 2003. Low flows and delta build-up have contributed to water supply problems for communities and industries along the river.

4

THOSE SANDBARS

All alluvial rivers (those with dirt banks and bottoms - see Appendix 5) continually erode their banks, especially on the outside of their bends, and continually build back land on the inside of the bends. They also deposit their excess sediment load in various parts of their main channels, which becomes sandbars.

The Missouri, being a typical alluvial river, did all of this eroding and building continuously. The vast plains of its watershed and its tributaries supplied it with a continued source of silt. The eroding and building along the river gradually moved the alluvium downstream (all the way to the Mississippi delta!). But, the re-supply was constant so the valley was in a state of equilibrium with no net loss or gain of the bottomland or sandbars.

The construction and operation of the dams completely changed the nature of the erosion and the building. The clear water discharged from the dams has the capacity of carrying more silt and thus the bank erosion of the vulnerable sites increased. The end of the high flood flows and the reduction of the silt load, as compared to pre-dam conditions, ended the building of the high bottomlands. Thus, there has been a net loss of the high bottom lands.

The river with its lower silt load can now sort the various soils. The finer particles, being more soluble, remain in suspension, and are transported downstream to the still water of the lake. There, they become the delta. The heavy, coarser soil particles, which we call sand, are deposited in the channel as sandbars. Thus, the bank-eroding river now results in a widening channel, an increase in sand bar area, and a net decrease of high bottomland. If this is allowed to continue, the river will become wider with no main channel and only many shallow channels. This has already happened at river mile 1,334, where the total channel width is over 3,000 feet. This will make boating difficult or impossible, at moderate or low river flows.

The pre-dam sandbars had a higher proportion of the fine silt and could be treacherous to man and beast. This is the quicksand that captured many larger animals, such as, deer, horses and cattle. The present sandbars,

Bank erosion along the Missouri River will ultimately result in a widening of the river and loss of a main channel.

which consist of a high percentage of course sand, are entirely different and can support humans, animals and even heavy equipment.

The pre-dam sandbars were usually flooded (and in a building stage) during the warm summer months when snow-melt water of the June rise traveled downstream. The flooded sandbars prevented growth on the bars and also prevented nesting of all shore birds. This was not the habitat of plovers, terns, geese or ducks. The lower river stages in the fall exposed the bare sandbars, and huge dust storms were common. Soil classifiers today note the difference in the soils east of the river because of the depositions of those dust storms by the prevailing west winds.

Now, the lower controlled summer flows expose the sandbars and allow summer nesting of shore birds. Plovers, terns and summer geese flocks are present.

However, the summer exposure of the sandbars allows vegetation to begin growing. This vegetation stops river-borne sediment during the higher river flows and many sandbars have aggraded enough to support willow, cottonwood, ash and box elder growth. Two good examples of this are near Bismarck along the east bank upstream from the I-94 bridge and along the west bank downstream from the Double Ditch Indian Village site.

Since the plovers and terns will not tolerate much vegetative growth on the sandbars, the newly formed bars are only a temporary habitat. If these bars are to continue to be useful to these birds, it is obvious that mechanical and/or chemical methods must be used to keep the sandbars bare. This should not be controversial considering the many non-natural methods currently used by wildlife interests to enhance or protect various species of wildlife.

One proposal is to allow high bottomland to continue to erode so more nest sandbars can be formed. The loss of irreplaceable high bottomland, the resulting increase in the dangerous Oahe delta, the loss of precious riverside habitat and the other negative affects on the river, obviously make this option entirely unacceptable.

Controlled summer water releases at the Garrison Dam now are moderate and constant to allow the shore birds to nest and prevent the flooding of their nests. These moderate and constant releases are also excellent for boaters, fishermen, irrigators and all river users. This is an example of a win-win situation for all.

There are over 30 vegetated sandbars in the Garrison to Oahe reach. Many of these already have major growths of cottonwoods and other trees and plants. These bars are sovereign land owned by the state which will increasingly become major wildlife habitat. Since they are public lands, they are also important hiking and exploring areas for nature lovers.

5

MYTHS, NOTIONS AND FALSEHOODS

"The Missouri is a large, powerful river. It will eventually wash away any rip-rap that is placed on its banks."
This is not true. There are many examples of rip-rap installed since 1960 that are performing well. The summer of 1997 was a supreme test when a 200-year event flowed through this reach with little or no damage to properly installed projects. Perhaps the best example is the bank protection that was installed upstream from the railroad bridge at Bismarck in 1885. This has protected the bridge with no repairs or additions. It is entirely grown over with trees now and actually is no longer required since the building of the Interstate-94 bridge immediately upstream.

In the 1980s the Corps installed several "demonstration" projects to test how little rock was required. Several of these did fail, as was expected, but the Corps learned from these projects. Perhaps the most economical method is to place the minimum amount of rock calculated and then add more later if needed. The first projects installed in the 1970s were copied after the installation along the navigation channel downstream, and were obviously over-designed for our area and thus unnecessarily expensive.

Controlling the river can be compared to building fences or corrals for cattle. If they are inadequate the cattle will break out, but if they are adequate the cattle will stay forever! There have been numerous suggestions for controlling the river by methods other than rocks, which are not considered "natural". Willows and grass planted on a sloping bank have been suggested. The Missouri is a large and powerful river and any method other than properly installed rock is only wasted effort and money. The recommended method of installing rock now is to provide adequate soil to be placed in all the voids between the rocks. Trees, shrubs and grass will quickly begin to grow and will cover the rocks. There are many examples of this on the older projects that have spontaneous growth on the rocks.

Another method that has been suggested is to use anchored round hay bales along the banks. This is the most ridiculous idea ever. Hay will quickly rot and can float away. It certainly cannot withstand the ice conditions we have at this latitude, and such an installation is certainly not natural.

"Protecting one curve of the river with rip-rap will simply bounce the river to the opposite bank and cause more bank erosions there."

The course of all alluvial rivers flowing in a broad valley will always develop into a series of "S" curves. The bank erosion occurs only on the outside of these curves where the water velocity and the centrifugal pressures against the banks are greatest. To prevent bank erosion, it is necessary to armor only these curves. It is true that this will deflect the currents to the opposite bank downstream and cause erosion there. But, this was already occurring as the river flowed through its series of "S" curves. The obvious solution is to protect the banks on the outside of all the curves. When this is accomplished, the great majority of bank erosion will be prevented.

There have been cases where a large, long jetty was installed in the upstream end of a curve. This worked fine in preventing erosion of that curve, but it concentrated the flow and increased the velocity of water deflected to the opposite bank downstream and greatly increased the erosion there. These large jetties are no longer used. Instead, the intention now is to follow along the present curve with the rip-rap and protect its banks without altering the characteristic of the flow downstream, although the downstream site may still require attention.

The design of bank protection here is entirely different then that installed in the navigation channel from Sioux City to St. Louis. There, the requirement was not only to stop bank erosion, but also to confine the river into a narrow channel of constant depth to ac-

While jetties did a fine job of preventing local bank erosion, they actually increased erosion of the opposite bank.

commodate large boats. Here, we only want to stop erosion where it is occurring and have no need or desire to disturb the banks where there is no erosion. Only about 40 percent of the 160 miles of banks need this protection. This will leave 100 miles of banks untouched and natural.

By the long and unique experience gained from the projects installed in our reach, the Corps is now capable of designing protection that will perform adequately at a minimum cost and with minimum disturbance to the natural river.

"We should not be using government funds to protect the banks and increase the value of the land to the private owner."

There are two things wrong with this statement. First, "government" funds will not be used. They will be Pick-Sloan Project funds and will be charged to the installation and maintenance of the entire project. It is now recognized (by the Corps' statements also) that installing the Pick-Sloan Project changed the nature of the river and that there is now a net loss of high bottomlands which did not occur previously. Therefore, project funds are appropriate. Also, the purpose of preventing erosion is not only to protect the affected land but also to prevent the building of the delta downstream from Bismarck. After the examples in Niobrara, Williston and now Pierre, the Bismarck delta will become critical if it is allowed to grow.

If we were to follow the logic of this notion we would also not build roads, schools, parks, etc. with government funds because they would enhance local values. One reason North Dakota agreed to the Pick-Sloan Project that took away 550,000 acres of land was the promised flood-proofing of the remaining 80 miles from Garrison to Oahe and the potential to develop that reach. It is now obvious that bank protection in the necessary locations is required to allow this development to occur and to prevent the loss of more valuable high bottomland, which is an endangered resource.

"The Missouri is the most (or the second most) endangered river in our nation."

This statement has been made many times by the American River Association, a preservation group based in Washington D.C. Apparently they base their statement on how the river compares to the river of Lewis and Clark's time and not on the overall change of the river good or bad. It is also ridiculous to place the entire Missouri with it's navigation channel, its chain of dams and their lakes, its remaining free flowing reaches and its mountain valley reaches into one category.

I would agree that the Missouri is perhaps one of the most changed rivers in the nation and that there are some negative aspects that remain to be modified or corrected. However, I don't hesitate to state that the Garrison to Oahe reach is or can be one of the most improved river reaches in the United States. A before and after comparison tells the story: floods vs. no floods, muddy water vs. clean water, game fish vs. rough fish, a recreation river (and sandbars) vs. poor conditions, a snag filled river vs. a clear channel, an endangered bird habitat vs. no summer habitat. Our great problem here is the continuing net loss of high bottomland and the continual building of the delta in south Bismarck/Mandan. This can, and obviously must be, corrected or greatly reduced by completing the protection of the river banks in the necessary locations.

A before and after comparison of each of the other reaches of the Missouri should be made and a good/bad decision made for each reach. The American Rivers statement therefore, is simplistic and not wholly credible.

"If not prevented there will be solid rows of houses from Oahe to the Garrison."

This is another statement that is made by those who do not understand the limitations placed by the river and its banks for acceptable housing locations.

Those who build on the river want consistent deep water and a protected bank. They also want dependable and good roads as well as access to electricity, phone and good water. County codes restrict building in areas below the 100-year flood levels (some now require 2 feet above the 100-year level). They also specify minimum lot sizes and soils acceptable for sewage disposal.

Also there are many reaches now in public and private ownership that will not allow housing developments.

Good examples of some of these restrictions are immediately upstream from the Interstate-94 bridge. The west bank is protected by rock rip-rap but is owned by the state and therefore will never be developed. The east bank composed of low vegetated sandbars is too low to allow housing and is also owned by the state back to the high bottomland and therefore, also cannot be developed. However, this low land is excellent wildlife habitat and is open for public exploration.

With these limitations, I estimate that not over 25 percent of the total river banks are available and suitable for housing. However, in the approved locations these homes are one of the developments that enhance the variety and the beauty of our river valley. The other seventy-five percent will remain untouched and natural.

"The amount of riverbank erosion is due to the amount of water released and is not affected by the way the same amount of water is released at the dam." The Corps made this statement in the Environmental Assessment for the Fort Peck flow modification mini-test dated April 2002 and in the Environmental Impact Statement for the Missouri River Master Water Control Manual dated August 2001. This statement is entirely false!

I requested a meeting in Bismarck of our Water Commission engineers, our BOMMM (Burleigh, Oliver, Mercer, McLean, and Morton County joint water resource board) engineer (all professional civil engineers), and myself with William Miller and John Remus (also professional civil engineers representing the Corps' Omaha office). The Corps engineers did agree that these statements were false and that the amount of bank erosion is greatly influenced by the way the same amount of water is released. I compare it to the reaction of a close friend of mine, whose doctor told him to limit himself to only one drink a day. He said one drink per day wasn't worth it. Instead he saved them up for the weekend and the inevitable happened. He could have tolerated one drink a day, but too much at one time was deadly!

This is why BOMMM has always requested that the Corps avoid low flows and then the inevitable high flows, since the amount of bank erosion will greatly increase with the same amount of water. When bank protection along the Garrison to Oahe reach is completed, the Corps can then have more freedom to vary the releases.

Why has the Corps made such a statement? Does it think that we don't know better and they could make their water releases without being concerned with the downstream consequences? I have submitted a written request to Col. Fastabend at Omaha that these false statements be acknowledged and corrected, but to date have not received a reply.

Bottom line – we should expect better from our U.S. Army Corps of Engineers!

"The river channel reduction and delta building at Bismarck will reach equilibrium and then all future delta formation will be downstream in Lake Oahe."

Yes, the Corps has stated this in its Oahe-Bismarck studies dated August 1985. It is obviously misleading and unsupported. There are, and have been, thousands of deltas in the world. They form and grow where the flowing water meets the still water of a lake or ocean and deposit their sediment load there. It is true that deltas grow both upstream and downstream, but they continue to grow as are the deltas at New Orleans and at Bismarck.

Does the Corps make statements like this because it wants to deny any responsibility, or do they not want to recommend and undertake delta elimination or reduction measures? Hundreds of millions of dollars worth of property in south Bismarck/Mandan are involved in this "Corps versus reality" controversy!

"There are no new cottonwoods growing in the Garrison to Oahe reach. Eventually, there will be no cottonwoods here."

There could be some validity to this statement. One reason North Dakota agreed to the Pick-Sloan project and the loss of 550,000 acres was the ability to develop the flood proofed Garrison to Oahe reach. Much of the high bottomland was cleared of brush and trees (including cottonwoods) and developed into highly productive farmland. Most owners left a fringe of trees along the river bank. However, in many locations the river continued to erode its banks and these trees were lost leaving only a naked bank.

There are still many acres of native forest remaining because the owners chose to preserve them. If the owner is a public entity these forests will never be destroyed. The Nature Conservancy purchased the Cross Ranch and is preserving the finest cottonwood forest I have seen. The trees there are healthy and not fire scared and will live for many decades. But if the public demands more cottonwoods they will simply have to purchase land and dedicate it to additional forests. Cottonwoods are easy to grow and do not necessarily need low wetland to germinate and grow.

Cottonwoods are the favorite food of beavers. They have destroyed many fine groves on the vegetated islands in the river. Any future attempt to grow the cottonwoods must include protection from beavers.

With desire and assistance of the public, cottonwoods can live in our valley.

Cottonwood with beaver damage. Beavers have destroyed many cottonwood stands along the Missouri River.

6

THE BOTTOM LINE

The installation of the Pick-Sloan dams on the Missouri River have certainly made it the most changed river in the nation, and in most cases, the most improved. This obviously is true of the Garrison to Oahe reach. However, if the delta situation at the Oahe headwaters is not controlled, we will come to doubt the "improved" description. Based on the evidence of the Niobrara, Williston, and Pierre deltas, the only question is when (and not if) the Bismarck delta will become intolerable unless every thing possible is done to reduce or stop the building of this mud dam.

Since over 90 percent of the soil transported into the delta originates from the upstream river banks, it is obvious that the bank protection projects there must be completed. According to Water Commission engineering figures, this would require armoring only 10 percent more of the total 180 miles of river banks at a cost of $13.8 million and would leave 60 percent (or 108 miles) of natural river bank.

Section 33 amendment to the Pick-Sloan Act, authorized, funded and directed the Corps to complete the needed bank protection. However, in its own interpretation of this law, the Corps refused to install these

Unprotected banks of the Missouri River near Bismarck, ND show the effects of erosion.

projects because they did not meet the Corps' favorable benefit-cost determination. This benefit-cost study was only site-specific and did not include the delta hazard, the reduction of hydro power revenues and the loss of recreation values of the river. If these were included, a favorable benefit-cost ratio would exist, although a favorable benefit-cost was not required in Section 33.

The BOMMM board has attempted to influence the Corps, as has North Dakota's congressional delegation, but the Corps seems to be a power unto itself and no change seems possible soon.

The Federal Fish and Wildlife Service, and our own North Dakota Game and Fish Department, also object to additional bank protection until "more studies are completed". Both entities are prime advisors to the Corps. Preservation groups such as the Sierra Club, the Wildlife Federation and many others also object to more bank protection.

A study in contrasts: portions of protected and unprotected bank. Also note, sandbar formation in the channel.

In recent years, BOMMM has met with these groups in various formats. It is obvious these groups want the river to remain like Lewis and Clark found it. They abhor any building along the river, which bank protection would allow.

Under these conditions no bank protection has been installed by the Corps in recent years and it is virtually impossible for private landowners to obtain permits from the Corps to install protection at their own expense. It is pathetic that a farmer using irrigation cannot get a permit to protect his pump nor can homeowners get permits to protect their homes. Meanwhile, bank erosion continues and the Bismarck delta keeps building. The Corps could be likened to the legendary Emperor Nero who played his fiddle while Rome burned!

What is the solution to this impasse? BOMMM has begun various efforts to bring all the river players together, and hopefully get some common sense decisions, but the outlook is not good. Perhaps some more drastic methods may be necessary.

Our North Dakota and South Dakota congressional delegations have introduced and secured passage of the Water Resources Development Act. When implemented it would establish a trust fund for the purpose of combating the sediment problems on the Missouri. This would provide funds, the use of which would be directed by an interstate established committee. It would take time to implement this Act, but it may be a long-term solution.

In the meantime, an affected riparian owner can, without a permit, bury rocks on his own land near the water. This would provide him with protection when or if the river erodes his bank. North Dakota law states that high bottomland is accretion and is not sovereign land and that the owner owns the land "over the bank". This would result in rough looking banks as compared to a permitted project, but may be the only way an owner can protect his land.

Stabilizing the banks of this reach is all-important, but also important is how the flows of the river are managed. The Corps has this responsibility and is governed by a Master Manual, which was developed in the beginning of the Pick-Sloan Project and is in the process of being updated. They must regulate the flows for flood control, hydropower production, industrial and irrigation supplies. In recent years, flow regulation for endangered species protection has been added and has taken priority over all other river uses. This is an alarming development.

One proposal in the new Master Manual would regulate the levels of Lake Oahe and Lake Sakakawea so that one lake would be rising during the spawning season while the other was receding. In order to produce such lake levels, this would mean above normal flows for our Garrison to Bismarck reach some years, and below normal flows other years.

We have become accustomed to and have enjoyed the moderate and stable summer flows to date. Allowing high flows followed by low flows would result in increased total bank erosion when compared to the current release pattern since bank erosion is an exponential function of the rate of water flow rather than proportional to water flow.

This type of flow pattern would be damaging to municipal and industrial water intakes and would also result in a reduction of summer uses such as boating and fishing. Finally, the low flows would allow the growth of more vegetation on sandbars, thus destroying significant shore bird habitat. It seems reasonable to object to policies which result in this type of flow management.

In recent years it is becoming harder to appreciate, evaluate, trust and understand the Corps. How can it prohibit the protection of upstream banks when the Bismarck delta continues to grow? How can it permit higher than necessary water releases at Garrison when it knows they will cause damaging downstream erosion? Why has it told us that the Garrison to Oahe bank erosion has greatly decreased and will soon stop when the river finds its channel? (The fact is that erosion has decreased, but only because of the bank protection installed to date. At the unprotected sites erosion has been, and will continue to be, undiminished unless protection is installed.) Why has the Corps told us that a delta is building at Bismarck but that it will only get so big and then the sediment load will be carried downstream. (It didn't work that way at New Orleans, Niobrara, Williston, or Pierre – and it won't at Bismarck!)

With all the history and evidence of delta formation why hasn't the Corps become proactive in doing all possible to prevent or delay the delta? The Corps recently got very black marks for its "study" of the locks on the Mississippi. The conclusion here is that the Water Commission engineers and many others in North Dakota will have to step up and be more involved in the Corps operations rather than depend on them.

The goal of the BOMMM board remains the same as it was when organized in 1983 and it is quite simple. Our goal is to prevent the loss of riparian land along the river. This will also accomplish many other important things. Prevention or reducing the growth of the Bismarck delta, preventing the loss of scenic and valuable wildlife habitat, preventing further reduction of hydroelectric winter releases at Garrison, allowing more variable water releases at Garrison without causing loss of land, causing the river to have a main channel rather than several small shallow channels, preventing the addition of more fallen trees (snags) into the river, protecting the clarity of the water and allowing permanent development along the river including establishment of vegetated buffer areas are all benefits of halting the erosion of the river banks.

There are more obstacles to BOMMM accomplishing this goal than when it started, but there are also many positives that will aid it in its efforts.

7

THE BOMMM
JOINT WATER RESOURCE BOARD

BOMMM is an acronym of the five counties along the Missouri River from Garrison Dam to the Oahe reservoir. They are Burleigh, Oliver, Mercer, McLean, and Morton. In 1983 these counties organized a joint water resource board under the laws of North Dakota with the main purpose being to promote the protection of land along the Missouri River in this reach. To date 30 percent of the banks of this reach have been protected with only 10 percent more needing protection.

During its tenure, BOMMM has issued several statements to promulgate its goals to others and to educate the public on river issues.

The following are some of these statements:

I. PLAN FOR BANK PROTECTION – GARRISON TO OAHE REACH

The Garrison Dam was closed in 1953 and Lake Sakakawea reached full operating levels in the mid-1960s. It soon became evident that the old pattern of slow bank erosion and the rebuilding of similar land below the dam had ended. The now clear water (which is released at times and in amounts most advantageous to downstream navigation, flood control, irrigation, recreation and environmental concerns) devoured the banks, especially at sharp curves during high flows. The building of a delta of the eroded soils in the upper end of Lake Oahe began. Only low sandbars were rebuilt and thus the net loss of valuable high bottomland began.

Congress has appropriated funds several times for bank protection projects. These federal projects, together with privately funded projects, protect 75 percent of the vulnerable sites. Resulting land loss is only one-fourth of what it would have been without the installed projects. However, the remaining unprotected sites continued to erode, especially in the high water years 1995, 1996, and 1997. The Oahe delta continues to build with water levels already one foot higher than in 1975 at the same flow rate. Allowable winter hydro discharges at Garrison are already reduced one-third due to the higher water level, and ice jam flooding during the fall freeze-up and the spring breakup due to the delta are an increasing concern.

Rip-rap along a stretch of Missouri River provides a stable bank.

II. LIMITED BANK PROTECTION

The BOMMM plan for the limited bank protection was and still is to install protection projects only in those critical areas that are actively eroding. We advocate the type of projects that meet approval of state and federal agencies and that are the least disruptive to river flows. The State Engineer has identified and prioritized the eroding sites. The estimated total cost of protecting those sites is $13.6 million. Perhaps more work needs to be done to identify and prioritize actively eroding sites that need protection.

Our plan also calls for leaving the remainder of the banks alone and to allow the river flows through and around the many sandbars and wooded islands on the river. Even after the identified eroding sites are protected, 60 percent of the total river bank miles will remain natural. Our plan recommends that the five counties involved who have zoning powers for the riparian land, require a uniform setback for all buildings along the river in their counties. We also recommend a program to allow purchasing development rights from willing riparian owners. (A similar program is being used to prevent urban sprawl in many states.) The recent President's budget recommends funding for purchasing environmental sensitive areas. It may be possible to utilize this program.

III. HIGH BOTTOMLAND, AN ENDANGERED RESOURCE: GARRISON TO OAHE- MISSOURI RIVER

The Garrison to Oahe reach high bottomlands must be classified as an endangered resource because they are:

    A. Unique – no other land in our state or nation has the same history of formation or characteristics.

B. Their amount is limited. North Dakota gave up 220 miles of high bottomland under Lake Sakakawea and Lake Oahe. Only 80 miles between Garrison and Oahe remain, and much of this has been or is being eroded away.

C. Without bank protection the high bottomland will be lost forever.

D. Once lost it can never be replaced, as is the case for endangered plant, fish and animal species.

E. One reason North Dakota agreed to give up the 550,000 acres of land, which the Pick-Sloan Project required, was the promised flood-proofing and the ability to develop the remaining high bottomland of the Garrison to Oahe reach. North Dakota deserves the protection of this land at Pick-Sloan Project expense.

IV. NEGATIVE EFFECTS OF ALLOWING BANKS TO ERODE

A. Permanent loss of high river bottomland. There is no possibility of these lands being rebuilt as they were during pre-dam conditions.

B. Permanent loss of vegetation, including cottonwood trees, other trees, bushes and grass on the land adjacent to the river. This is a habitat of bald eagles, other birds and other wildlife.

C. Threat of land loss prevents or discourages utilization of adjacent land for agricultural, commercial and residential uses.

D. Soils of the eroded banks are carried downstream and are deposited as a delta in the headwaters of the Oahe. This has the following effects:

    a.   Increasing higher water tables in land near

the delta, which is highly developed for commercial and residential uses. There already are higher water tables in Bismarck, including the Bismarck Law Enforcement Center. The delta in Williston is much more advanced than the Bismarck delta, and this should be a wake-up call for the Bismarck area!

b.   Reduction in river channel capacity under ice in the winter has already reduced valuable winter electrical generation capacity at Garrison Dam by one-third.

c.   Reduction in summer channel capacity, which is extremely necessary to transmit high flood flows such as in the summer of 1997.

d.   Reduction in dam capacity of Lake Oahe. The Corps estimates that 3,000-acre feet of soils are being added to Lake Oahe each year. This reduces the kilowatt-hour capacity of the Oahe generation station and represents an increasing financial loss to the project.

E. Continued bank erosion will allow the river to develop into many small, shallow channels and no main channel, which will make boating difficult, even during higher Garrison Dam discharges. This has already happened in areas such as at river mile 1,334.8 where the river is 3,000 feet wide and has no main channel.

F. Bank erosion places the falling soils into the stream causing chemical and clarity reduction of water quality.

G. Trees and other debris being deposited in the river making boating dangerous and difficult.

V. POSITIVE EFFECTS OF ALLOWING BANKS TO ERODE

A. Fish biologists claim eroded soils and vegetation provide habitat and food for fish. However, even with three-fourths of the needed bank protection already installed, the Garrison to Oahe reach has developed into a world-class walleye fishery. Apparently the tributary and local run-off is furnishing the necessary habitat and food.

Considering the above stated facts, we should not allow the loss of more high bottomlands (see Appendix 2) and the damage the eroded soils will cause.

IV. ENDANGERED SPECIES ON THE GARRISON TO OAHE REACH OF THE MISSOURI RIVER

The three endangered species identified on the Garrison to Oahe reach are the Pallid Sturgeon (fish), the Least Tern and the Piping Plover (birds).

The sturgeon was native to the pre-dam Missouri River. Its habitat then, for which it was well-suited, included the muddy water all year and the warm water in the spring, summer and fall. Being a bottom feeder, its limited vision was not important and the muddy water protected it from predator fish.

The Garrison Dam with its discharge of cold, clear water changed the habitat entirely. The clear water allowed predator fish (mostly walleye) to feed on the sturgeon eggs and their young, and the cold water is not conducive to sturgeon egg laying and hatching.

With the drastic change in river character it is obvious that this river can no longer be a sturgeon habitat. Any attempt to reintroduce this fish here (except for removing the dam) will be futile and time and money should not be expended here.

Fortunately, there is a bright side to the sturgeon problem. The many tributaries of the Missouri and the river below Omaha do retain the muddy, warm, summer water that is sturgeon habitat. Here, efforts should be successful in maintaining the sturgeon.

The pre-dam Missouri River was not a habitat, or at best was an extremely poor habitat, for the terns and plovers. They required bare sandbars near water for their nesting sites.

Except for the extreme drought years, the summer snow melt "June rise" covered all sandbars from late May to early August which were the required nesting dates of these birds. Therefore, these conditions allowed little or no plover or tern propagation here.

Lewis and Clark reported these shore birds here, but they traveled this reach during October when the birds were congregating on the bare sandbars from other nesting sites for their migrating flight.

Garrison Dam Powerhouse. The dam was closed in 1953 creating Lake Sakakawea. Work on the dam was completed in 1955.

The construction and operation of the Garrison Dam and the regulated flows of this reach now allow sandbars to be bare during the nesting period of these birds and suddenly they have the desired habitat.

The Corps, to protect this habitat, is compelled to maintain moderate flows with no sandbar flooding throughout the summer months. This is ideal for the birds, ideal for the irrigators, ideal for the boaters, ideal for the fisherman and ideal for city and industrial water supplies. We should appreciate this unique situation when protection of an endangered species is also highly desirable to all other users of an area.

There is, however, one problem to this operation. Bare sandbars, when not covered with water during the growing season, quickly sprout and grow bar willows and other vegetation making them unsuitable habitat.

The river has in the past created some new sandbars from soil derived from bank erosion. In 1997, the 200-year flow of the river and the increased bank erosion produced many bars. But depending on more erosion of the high banks to produce more sandbars is unacceptable. There is not only the continued loss of irreplaceable land, but also much of the eroded soils increase the now recognized dangerous Oahe delta in south Bismarck.

The obvious solution is the control of vegetation by mechanical or chemical means on some of the thousand of acres of vegetated sandbars in the Garrison to Oahe reach. These sandbars are sovereign land and are readily available to those who wish to enhance the Plover and Tern habitat.

The 1,390 miles of shoreline around Lake Sakakawea and the 2,250 miles around Lake Oahe are also a tremendous addition to shore bird habitat. Their future should be assured!

The Corps should be urged to continue the highly successful pattern of moderate, steady Garrison releases through the summer months.

Delta buildup in south Bismarck.

VII. THE CASE FOR PICK-SLOAN PROJECT FINANCING OF MISSOURI RIVER BANK PROTECTION ON THE GARRISON DAM TO OAHE REACH

In an August 1977 report to Congress on the Three Forks, Montana to Sioux City, Iowa reach of the Missouri River, the Corps explained the bank erosion problem:

"In the natural river prior to the construction of the reservoirs, there was balance over the years between the destruction of valley lands by bank erosion and sediment deposited during the floods. This process resulted in a continual migration of the river channel within the Missouri River Valley. Due to the balance between the erosion and the deposition processes, however, there was no long-term net loss of high valley lands.

Since the dam closures, the operation of the reservoir system has eliminated both the floods and the sediment that were essential for the building process. On the other hand, the erosion of high banks continues. Consequently, bank erosion results in a permanent net loss of high valley lands that are never replaced elsewhere in the valley as in the era before the reservoirs. High valley lands are being converted to river channel and sand bar areas, and the width between high banks continues to grow. This process, unless halted, would eventually transform the present river into a wide area of sandbars and channels, occupying an increasing proportion of the valley width between cliffs."

The conclusion is that the Pick-Sloan Project is now causing a net loss of high bottomland.

Another related problem that is becoming more critical in recent years is the building of a delta in the headwaters of the Oahe by the soil eroded from the upstream banks. A year 2000 study by the United States Geological Survey at Bismarck, reported over 90 percent of the soil being deposited in the Oahe delta came from the banks and bottom of the Missouri River and less than 10 percent came from the Knife, Heart and other tributaries. This delta has already raised the river levels south of Bismarck one foot higher than it was in 1983 for the same river flows. The rising groundwater tables and the threat of both fall and spring ice-jam flooding has caused and will continue to cause drastic problems for the highly developed adjacent areas.

The Oahe delta has forced the reduction of winter water releases at Garrison by one-third, thereby greatly reducing high-priced water power revenues and reducing the flexibility of releases at Garrison. Unless the delta growth is stopped it will continue and become extremely critical. A similar delta is building at Williston, but it is much more advanced because of the high silt load of the Yellowstone. It is causing great problems there. A delta has also formed immediately below Pierre in the upper reach of the Big Bend Dam reservoir. Congress has appropriated $38 million for the buy-out of up to 200 homes there. The entire town of Niobrara, Nebraska was moved out after only twelve years of Pick-Sloan due to the delta there. These deltas should be a wake-up call for the control of the Oahe delta at Bismarck.

VIII. JUSTIFICATION

A. North Dakota gave up 550,000 acres of prime land so the Pick-Sloan Project could be built. A North Dakota State University Study (Agricultural Economics Report No. 190) reveals the state is also losing more than $500 million in gross business volume annually that the flooded land would have produced.

B. North Dakota was promised a Garrison Diversion Project as mitigation, but to date very little has been accomplished. We were promised economical hydroelectric power for our rapidly developing rural electric cooperatives. This has been and is being delivered, although a strong case can be made that North Dakota is not receiving a fair share of the power from the dams. North Dakota was also promised flood protection for the remaining Garrison to Oahe reach of the river valley so land along the reach could be developed. Flood protection has been achieved, as was demonstrated by flood control in the valley during the 1997 200-year flood event (see graph on page 5). However, unless this reach receives bank protection where needed, and as the Oahe delta continues to grow, the promise of utilizing this reach will be diminished.

C. Downstream, all the banks have been protected from Sioux City to St. Louis by the Pick-Sloan

Project at a cost of $750,000 per mile (1960s dollars). This was done for navigation and for protection of adjacent land. Seventy-five percent of the cost was charged to land protection and only 25 percent to navigation development. Levees and pumps have been added where needed. The downstream bank protection and flood control has allowed intensive development of the high bottomland there. This is in contrast to our North Dakota reach where we continue to lose land and development is discouraged or prevented. The Garrison to Oahe reach was entirely forgotten in the Pick-Sloan Project.

D. To date the Corps estimates the Pick-Sloan Project has prevented over $22 billion in flood damages.

E. A 1997 North Dakota State Water Commission Survey estimated only $13.8 million would be required to complete the protection of the Garrison to Oahe area.

F. $150 to $200 million worth of hydroelectric power is produced annually. Repayment of hydroelectric costs to the project is on schedule.

G. Congress has appropriated funds to the Corps to install protection where needed and charge it to the Pick-Sloan Project (Section 33 Funds). However, the Corps (contrary to Section 33 verbage) has refused to install protection unless it has a favorable benefit/cost ratio. The Corps study did not consider the delta effect, the reduction of winter power revenues, and the destruction of prime wildlife habitat.

H. Benefit/cost studies that include potential land values, habitat losses, loss of hydroelectric revenues, and the Oahe delta problem can have a positive value.

I. There are many precedents for remedying problems on the Pick Sloan Project and other federal projects. Three important cases are the removal of the entire town of Niobrara, the buy-out of the Buford-Trenton irrigation project at Williston, and the buy-out of south Pierre. All were precipitated by deltas that created high groundwater tables.

IX. OTHER FACTS

A. Continued bank erosion has destroyed and will destroy many wooded areas along the river. Some of these are bald eagle nesting areas and prime wildlife habitat.

B. There is absolutely no intention to straitjacket the river with revetment on both sides. We don't want our river to become a narrow navigation channel as was done from Sioux City to St. Louis.

C. Seventy-five percent of the needed bank protection has already been installed using Pick-Sloan Project and private funds. Therefore, land loss and the Oahe delta formation was only one-fourth of what it would have been without this protection in the high waters of 1995, 1996, and 1997.

D. The dam and the installed bank protection have transformed this river from a big, muddy catfish and carp fishery to a clear, cool, world famous walleye, pike, trout and salmon fishery. It is also great for other recreation and all other uses. The river will continue to run through and around the many wooded islands and bare sandbars as it does now, even if the remaining "hot spots" are controlled. The fishery and wildlife habitat should continue to improve!

E. Since 75 percent of the required revetment is already in place and the positive effect on the river and adjacent habitat is obviously apparent, no time and money should be wasted on studies and flood threats.

F. Under North Dakota law (NDCC 47-06-05 and 61-33-01), the adjacent land is privately owned down to the waters edge. The counties have zoning power over the adjacent land, and the Corps and the state engineer control the river and the wooded islands and sandbars.

G. The American Rivers Association has recently declared the Missouri river the most endangered river in the United States. We entirely disagree with this organization especially for the Garrison to Oahe reach. Clear vs. muddy water, floods vs. no floods and walleye vs. carp clearly say that this is the most improved river in the nation. However, hardening the remaining unprotected banks will make this an idyllic river.

X. SHORE ZONE OWNERSHIP

Hindsight tells us that North Dakota should have insisted on bank protection as part of the bargain of giving up 550,000 acres of land. However, we are very critical of the Corps because it should have known troublesome deltas would form in the upper ends of its lakes, especially after what has happened at Niobrara, Pierre, Williston and now Bismarck. The Corps should have begun immediate action to prevent or reduce the deltas. After 50 years, it is apparent that even more drastic action must be taken soon, such as lowering the operating level of the dams or more very expensive buyouts.

The area between the low water mark and the ordinary high water mark of a lake or stream is called the shore zone. It is accepted that the water, the river or lake bottom and the islands are sovereign land and are owned by the public. The ownership of the shore zone, however, continues to be unclear, especially along the Missouri. The "ordinary high water mark" is usually defined as the location of change of vegetation along the shore, but certainly is a very indefinite term. The fact that the Garrison to Oahe river levels are controlled by the releases at Garrison makes the ordinary high water mark term even more ambiguous. The entire area below the high water mark is being described as sovereign land by some entities.

Before North Dakota statehood, the federal government owned all sovereign land. At the time of statehood the government deeded this sovereign land to the state. North Dakota, at that time, gave the land between the low water mark and the ordinary high water mark to the adjacent landowner. Therefore, it would appear that the adjacent landowner also owns the shore zone. However, some legal opinions state that North Dakota was not legally able to give this shore zone and therefore the ownership of the shore zone remains with the state.

To further strengthen the case of the landowner, North Dakota law states that accretion land (land built by the action of the river- this would include almost all land along the Garrison to Oahe reach) is not sovereign land and that the ownership extends "over the bank" (ND law 47-06-05 and 61-33-01).

The conclusion here must be that, until the Supreme Court decides otherwise, the adjacent landowner has ownership down to the water's edge. Unfortunately, some state and federal entities, apparently feeling that the case for the adjacent landowner is illegal, are claiming the shore zone.

It is unfortunate that the shore zone ownership is being challenged. It would be in the best interest of all involved if the legal ownership could be finally determined.

XI. OUR NEIGHBORS

The Pick-Sloan Project left 80 miles in North Dakota as a free-flowing river. It also left 120 miles between the Ft. Peck Dam in Montana and Williston, and the sixty miles between Yankton, South Dakota and Sioux City, Iowa free-flowing. The river from Sioux City to St. Louis is also free-flowing, but it has been rip-rapped on both banks to prevent bank erosion and to maintain a narrow and constant depth channel for navigation.

The free-flowing reaches in Montana, North and South Dakota were entirely omitted from the Pick-Sloan Plan although they are drastically affected by it. The Ft. Peck reach is similar to our North Dakota reach. The river is smaller (our river minus the Yellowstone) but has a slightly steeper slope, which means faster river currents. The bank erosion problems are similar to ours with the excess sediment being deposited in the Williston area. As the Corps' engineers finally admitted to us, the amount of bank erosion depends on the nature of the releases at Ft. Peck and not just the total amount of water.

The environmentalists have succeeded in introducing a plan for water releases at Ft. Peck to enhance the propagation of the pallid sturgeon, an endangered species. The plan calls for releasing 11,000 cubic feet per second (cfs) over the top of the dam and 4,000 cfs through the power-house during the month of June. The warmer water from the top of the lake would mix with the colder bottom water and together with the higher flows would duplicate the pre-dam conditions and thus enhance the spawning characteristics of the river.

There is, however, a high price for this plan. The water being released over the top of the dam would not generate hydropower. The Corps states that $2.5 million of income would be lost each year. The higher-than-usual releases would greatly increase downstream bank erosion and increase the sediment deposition at the Williston area as compared to the present release pattern at Ft. Peck

This is another example of where no benefit-cost studies are required for the endangered species, and yet the Corps has required these types of benefit-cost studies for other river projects!

The South Dakota-Nebraska reach has a different problem. There the river is larger and perhaps has even greater fluctuations than our North Dakota reach to accommodate downstream flooding and navigation requirements. There the bank erosion is also a huge problem. Since there are no dams downstream the sediment is carried downstream and is eventually deposited in the Mississippi delta at New Orleans.

Several years ago, because of the alarming bank erosion, part of this reach signed an agreement with the National Park Service. The Park Service agreed to rip-rap the banks if the owners would forgo any development along the river. The owners have maintained their agreement but the Park Service has not. It is still debating about what type of revetment to use and allowing even more land to be lost in the meantime. These are very troubled times for the reach because of the lack of a proactive attitude by responsible entities.

The lakes behind the three dams in southern South Dakota are shorter and much smaller than the lakes behind Garrison and Oahe. The sediment accumulation there has reached a point where some predict only 50 to 75 years before the entire lakes will be filled and useless as storage for flood control and navigation uses.

To address this alarming sediment problem, South Dakota river users have formed Missouri Sediment Action Coalition. The Coalition's goal is to have the Corps to finally recognize and address the sediment problem. It has not recommended any specific method, but expects the expertise of the Corps to cope with the problem. Since dredging would be extremely expensive, the obvious plan now is for reduction of the sediment entering the lakes. This may include increased soil conservation along and additional retention dams and bank protection on the tributaries.

BOMMM has joined the South Dakota coalition. BOMMM's goal is the same and the increased pressure on the Corps should be important to all concerned.

8

GARRISON TO OAHE:
THE MOST IMPROVED RIVER IN THE NATION

The American Rivers Association has declared the Missouri River the most ruined, and now the second most ruined, river in America. This classification is easily refuted. First, the Missouri River was and is too large and too variable to be put into one category; and second, it certainly does not apply to the Garrison to Oahe reach.

To make an evaluation one must know how it was before Pick Sloan and compare it to now. I am uniquely qualified to make this comparison since I have lived with the river since 1931. Garrison Dam was closed in 1953 so I learned to know it well then and all the years since.

The old river was correctly named the "Old Muddy" or "Big Muddy" since it carried a full load of sediment. It did erode its banks, although much slower than we are led to believe. But being an honest river, it always built back as much as it took so there was no net loss of land. Ice-jam flooding was common in the spring, making any use of the land other than limited agricultural and recreational use impossible. Before the era of the Pick-Sloan dams, the water from mountain snowmelt and the June rise came through the summer months. While it did not flood the high bottomland, it inundated all sandbars each year except in the extreme drought years. This made nesting of plovers, terns and geese difficult to impossible. The fishery was catfish, carp, bullheads, sturgeon and other muddy water lovers.

In contrast, our modern river now has clear, cold water controlled by the Garrison Dam releases. Flooding has ceased as was proven in 1997 when a 200-year water flow was safely passed through without flooding the high bottomlands. Agricultural, commercial and residential development of the former flood plain has flourished. With the exception of years like 1997, the summer river now has bare and vegetated sand bars and islands that provide excellent nesting for the plovers, terns, geese and other birds. The shores of Lake Sakakawea and Lake Oahe have also added nesting habitat (Lake Sakakawea has 1,340 shore miles at 1,837 feet of elevation, and Lake Oahe has 2,250 shore miles at 1,607 feet of elevation). The carp, bullheads and sturgeon, no longer compatible with the clear, cold water, are gone. In their place is a world-class walleye, sauger and northern pike fishery. The most improved river title is obviously deserved.

Is the river perfect?

No, there are problems with accelerated bank erosion caused by the clear water and delta formation in Oahe's headwaters. Fortunately, three-fourths of the needed bank protection is already in place and our BOMMM group is promoting completion of the remaining needed protection. At that time 60 percent of the bank will still remain natural.

Our reach will then become the gem of our nation!

9

BOMMM'S CONTINUING EFFORTS

Installing the needed rip-rap on the Missouri banks to save the riparian land from destruction and determining the ownership of the shore zone were the goals of BOMMM when it was organized in 1983. Individual county water resource boards and then BOMMM have had some success in installing rip-rap in many locations. The North Dakota State Engineer's study determined that three-fourths of the needed rip-rap has been installed. This was financed with specific appropriations by Congress but was never, at the Corps' insistence, connected to the Pick-Sloan Project. Further, in some locations the rip-rap installations were to be maintained by the local water boards or the state.

BOMMM never agreed to this financing method, especially when the Sioux City to St. Louis reach received full bank protection with its maintenance at Pick-Sloan expense. However, the need was so critical that the local projects were installed and the maintenance responsibility is still unsettled or variable.

BOMMM's greatest success (or so we thought at the time) was securing the passage of the Section 33 amendment to the Pick-Sloan Project through the leadership of then Senator Burdick of North Dakota. This amendment provided funding and directed the Corps to install the needed protection and charge it to the Pick-Sloan Project. However, the Corps decided the specified bank protection didn't meet its criteria and refused to act in spite of Senator Burdick's efforts. This impasse continues.

In recent years the emergence of the environmental movement, the preservationists in many disguises, and those citing the endangered species law have advised the Corps not to permit any additional rip-rap "until we study it more." This has prevented the issuance of any additional permits, even when the riparian owner was paying for the rip-rap to prevent loss of critical land!

BOMMM had two choices: either sue the Corps (if it could get sufficient finances) to complete the needed rip-rap as directed by the section 33 law; or to bring all those who have interest in the river together to try to reach some acceptable solution.

BOMMM chose the latter and has hosted numerous meetings in recent years with this broad group to explore if some method of sav-

Erosion contributes to sediment and delta creation as well as loss of habitat. Here, the river is about to claim another cotton-wood which will no doubt become a hazard to navigation.

65

ing the endangered land that meets the Corps' requirements can be formulated. To date, these meetings have been informative to all, but most of those involved have their own agenda and little or no compromise seems possible. It has become obvious that the objection to more rip-rap is the increased development of the high bottomland that would follow. The preservationists, of course, do not want this.

BOMMM is exploring the possibility of installing a demonstration rip-rap project on state prison land south of Bismarck. Before-and-after studies could then be made. Since there would be no development on this state-owned land, all of the "players" have approved this proposal. The Corps has a special program for this type of project and with the state could fund this project. If this demonstration project could be accomplished it might lead to the permitting and installation of more needed rip-rap

BOMMM, with the cooperation of the Water Commission and the North Dakota Water Education Foundation, has also developed a concept plan for our river. This is not a plan for development, but only a broad collection of facts and opportunities for the Garrison to Oahe reach. BOMMM is also exploring the development of a Comprehensive Plan. This would contain recommendations and plans for the river corridor development. The Comprehensive Plan would take several years to complete and would require the input of all the BOMMM counties and especially the riparian owners. The goal of protecting private property owners' rights could be lost if the present do-nothing conditions continue. Financing for the Comprehensive Plan could come from the Missouri River Trust Legislation (which North Dakota Senator Kent Conrad worked to get passed), and from the counties and the Water Commission. BOMMM will continue its efforts to save the endangered land along our river.

10

THE NEXT 50 YEARS

After the last glacier melted, the Missouri gradually reached equilibrium between the silt load and the water it was obliged to carry and the size of its channel through the high bottomland. This status remained unchanged for about the eight thousand years before Lewis and Clark "discovered" our river. It eroded its bank on the outside of the curves and built back an equal amount on the inside of the downstream curves. The trees on the banks were in turn sacrificed into the river and then were reestablished on the newly developing land. The wildlife and the human population had little or no effect on the river but merely lived with what it, and the high bottomland provided.

For almost 150 years after Lewis and Clark, the river was little altered by the increasing human presence, but the Pick-Sloan Project with its chain of dams abruptly changed all that.

We know how the river has changed in the fifty years of this new regime, but we must realize that this change is only in mid-course and we have to ponder what kind of river and adjacent land we will have in the next 50 years. Now that humans have control of the river and the riparian land, the future of our valley is up to us.

The Corps controls how the water is released at the Garrison Dam and that influences all aspects of our valley. The Corps also controls the permits and can influence the financing of the rip-rap protection for the eroding banks. In addition, it controls the permitting of municipal, industrial and irrigation water intakes and boat docks.

As I have previously explained, until court action declares otherwise, private owners have almost complete control of the land down to the waters edge where ever it is. They cannot, however, make any installations in the water without Corps approval.

Each county along the river has zoning authority for plotting developments along the river. They are each in the process of evaluating their codes and will, no doubt, confirm or update them.

What, then must be done to design our valley to serve most of the people for the next 50 years and after?

The first and most dangerous problem that must be addressed is the building delta in south Bismarck/ Mandan. Because of its relatively slow building we have some time to deal with this delta compared to the other Pick-Sloan deltas. Obviously, the eroding upstream banks must be rip-rapped since this is where over 90 percent of the silt load originates. Until the banks are protected, we must demand that the Corps regulate the releases at Garrison to minimize erosion and to minimize the increase of the delta. The unbalanced dam level proposal, with its extremely high flows some years and the increased bank erosion it would cause, should not be allowed until the banks are protected. The Garrison to Oahe users should perhaps permanently object to the unbalanced dam scheme since the high flows some years, and the low flows other years, negatively affect the summer uses of our river. The stable summer flows, such as the Corps has maintained in the past to respect the endangered bird habitat, should be continued. This is great for boaters, fishermen, irrigators and all summer river users. Some sandbars must have mechanical or chemical control of growth to maintain the habitat of the plovers and terns.

As previously mentioned, sites along the river suitable for home building are very limited. Most of these suitable sites will likely be utilized in future years. Burleigh County has recently decided on a 75-foot setback for homes. This seems to be a reasonable compromise between on-the-water or in-the-woods homes. The main goal is that all adjacent homes have the same setback in their platted development. Unfortunately, trees grow slowly and it will take another 50 years to develop a pleasing frontage. Growth in and on the rocks of the older rip-rap installations demonstrates what can be expected in the future. All future rip-rap installations should include filling the voids between the rocks with soil to promote tree and shrub growth there.

There have been some who want to prevent more development on the river. One proposal (by land owners) would allow owners to sell perpetual nondevelopment easements of their river-front and retain all other rights to their river-front land. Unfortunately, the legislatures in 2001 and 2003 have refused to allow these easements. This would have been a win-win for all interests. We hope this will be authorized in the future so that more river frontage can remain untouched.

There have been many requests for more river access for the public. Again, deep-water protected suitable sites are limited, but they can be purchased and developed. Little has been done to authorize and fund additional access. This must be accomplished so more of the public will be able to enjoy our river. The unvegetated sandbars are used now and will in the future by the boating public, although they are to in competition with the terns and plovers. Some bars, especially those that are maintained for use by shore birds, could be restricted from public use. The longer, older islands, some of which are becoming increasingly heavily wooded, are now the least used area in our valley. Maintained hiking trails through these public lands and developing public boat access to them can furnish the public a new and fascinating experience.

What will be our status 50 years from now? Will we have achieved the companion goal of stopping more bank erosion and more delta building? Will we have controlled the limited developable sites for their best use? Will the tree and shrub growth on permanent land and rocks add a feel of beauty and permanence to our valley? Will the Corps, in planning the water releases at Garrison, make the effects on our reach a high priority? Will we have developed the sandbars and islands for the maximum enjoyment by our public and use by the endangered species? Will we have laws that allow land owners to sell nondevelopment easements of the river banks? Will we have defined the ownership of the shores so both the landowner and the river user knows their rights?

Accomplishing these goals will require much increased proactivity by our state engineer, the Water Commission, our governor, our national and state legislators, and especially by the Corps and all of us directly affected by the future of the river and the delta. If these goals are achieved in the next 50 years (much sooner would be desirable), then we will have a river that will not only provide the greatest good for the most people, but also will be in a condition to continue doing so for countless more decades. The Missouri River Valley's future is up to us!

Over 350 Years of Missouri River Use & Policy

1650 The first irrigation in the Missouri River basin likely started by Native American tribes along Ladder Creek in northern Scott County, Kansas.

1803 President Jefferson purchases the Louisiana Territory from France. Missouri River basin is nearly two-thirds of the purchase.

1804 President Jefferson assigns U.S. Army officers Meriwether Lewis and William Clark to lead the Corps of Discovery through the Missouri basin to the Northwest. The Corps winters with Mandan Indians near present-day Washburn, North Dakota.

1824 U.S. Supreme Court opinion in Gibbons v. Ogden: "The power of Congress... comprehends navigation, within the limits of every State in the Union; so far as that navigation may be, in any manner, connected with 'commerce with foreign nations, or among the several States, or with the Indian tribes.'" Federal authority over navigation includes control of all navigable waters of the U.S. Also includes authority over nonnavigable tributaries if the navigable capacity of navigable waterways is affected, or if interstate commerce is otherwise affected. Also in 1824, Congress authorizes the U.S. Army Corps of Engineers (Corps) to aid navigation on the Nation's waterways. "Snagging" work on the Missouri River begins in 1838.

1844 The flood of 1844 is thought to be the greatest ever in the lower Missouri River basin. Although accurate records are not available, the flooded river is estimated to have discharged 900,000 cubic feet per second at its mouth.

1862 the first 160-acre land grand under the Homestead Act is made to Daniel Freeman near Beatrice, Nebraska Territory.

1866 Congress enacts legislation stating "whenever... rights to the use of water for mining, agriculture, manufacturing, or other purposes, have vested and accrued, and the same are recognized and acknowledged by the local customs, laws, and the decisions of courts, the possessors and owners of such vested rights shall be maintained and protected in the same." Congress recognizes the acquisition of water by prior appropriation for a beneficial use, as prevalent in much of Missouri basin, was entitled to protection.

1869 Completion of the first transcontinental railroad through the Missouri River basin fosters settlement in the region.

1872 Railroad reaches Bismarck, North Dakota.

1897 Corps Captain Hiram Chittenden, submits report upon the practicability and desirability of constructing reservoirs in upper Missouri basin. He concludes upstream reservoir construction was "an indispensable condition to the highest development" of the region.

1889 Director of the U.S. Geological Survey John Wesley Powell urges development of irrigation in the Dakotas and Montana stating "No water falling within these upper basin states should flow beyond their boundaries."

1902 Reclamation Act establishes public policy of irrigation in the Dakotas by authorizing the Secretary of the Interior to locate, construct, operate and maintain works for the storage, diversion, and development of waters for the reclamation of arid and semi-arid lands in the western States.

1903-1905 Missouri River floods.

1906 The Secretary of the Interior is authorized to develop hydroelectric generation at reclamation projects where needed for irrigation.

1908 Missouri River floods.

1908 In Winters v. U.S., relating specifically to Indian reserved water rights, the Supreme Court states federal government has the constitutional power to "reserve the waters and exempt them from appropriation under the state laws" beginning at the time lands were withdrawn from the public domain.

1915 Missouri River floods.

1925 The Rivers and Harbors Act of 1925 authorizes the Corps and the Federal Power Commission to consider needs for irrigation in planning for navigation, water power, and flood control.

1927 Congress authorizes Corps to undertake comprehensive river basin studies known as "308" reports. The reports are to recommend development for the purposes of navigation, flood control, hydroelectric power, and irrigation.

1930 Drought period in the Missouri basin is of longer duration than any previously recorded.

1933 Corps issues 308 Report on Missouri River basin-H.Doc.238, Seventy-third Congress, 1933- that is keystone technical sourcebook. Corps recommends Fort Peck, Montana, "be built to the maximum practicable capacity and be operated primarily for navigation, with such arrangement for future installation of power as will permit the maximum production of hydroelectric power constant with the primary demands of navigation." President Roosevelt uses report and authority under provisions of National Industry Recovery Act to initiate project construction of first main stem federal dam on Missouri River. Congress formally approved this action in 1935.

1936 Roosevelt creates the Great Plains Committee to recommend ways to ameliorate the effects of drought, depression, and poor land use practices plaguing much of the Missouri River basin. The Committee's report, published in 1940 by the National Resources Planning Board, recommends among other things, additional irrigation projects and detailed planning.

1936 Flood Control Act declares flood control to be a proper federal activity; that improvements for flood control purposes are in the interest of the general welfare; that the federal government should improve or participate in the improvement of navigable waters or their tributaries for flood control "if the benefits to whomsoever they may accrue are in excess of the estimated costs, and if the lives and social security of people are otherwise adversely affected." The Act prescribes those federal investigators and improvements of rivers and other waterways should be under the jurisdiction of the Corps.

1938 Congress authorizes the installation of hydroelectric generating facilities at Fort Peck.

1938 First "comprehensive" plan for flood control and other purposes in the Missouri basin, as set forth in Flood Control Committee Document 1, Seventy-fifth Congress, 1937, is adopted by Congress which includes a system of reservoirs on Missouri Valley tributary streams in the lower basin.

1939 The Reclamation Project Act, Section 9, authorizes the Bureau of Reclamation (BOR) to plan for the conservation, control, and use of water resources in the Missouri basin and permits BOR to allocate part of reclamation project costs for flood control and navigation. The resulting plan, known as the "Sloan Plan" after its primary author William Glenn Sloan (BOR Billings, MT office Assistant Director) is presented to Congress in 1943.

1939 Board of Engineers for Rivers and Harbors recommends a nine-foot by 300-foot navigation channel on the Missouri River from Souix City to the mouth.

1942 The Missouri River States Commission organizes. The Committee eventually includes all ten-basin states represented by the states' governors and their technical advisers. Their goal is management of the river for the greatest common good of the basin and the nation.

1943 Missouri River flooding prompts the U.S. House of Representatives to ask Corps to review previous plans. The Corps' Missouri River Division office in Omaha, Nebraska, submits House Document 475, which becomes known as the "Pick Plan" after Missouri River Division Engineer, Colonel Lewis A. Pick.

1944 The Missouri River States Committee submits a resolution to Congress through President Roosevelt calling for: 1) a single comprehensive plan for Missouri basin development, 2) the Corps and BOR to coordinate and merge their plans, 3) legislation to implement the basin wide development plan, and 4) the beneficial consumptive use of basin water arising in states wholly or partially west of the 98th meridian to have precedence over water for navigation. Roosevelt endorses the resolution in his transmittal to Congress and adds his recommendation for a Missouri Valley Authority.

1944 Corps and BOR representatives meet in Omaha on October 16-17 and merge their plans. The combined plan is submitted to Congress as Senate Document 247 and is enacted into law on December 22 as part of the Flood Control Act of 1944 (P.L. 534, 78th Congress). The Plan calls for construction of 112 dams having a total storage of 107 million acre-feet of water, 4.3 million acres of irrigation, 2.6 million kilowatts of hydroelectric generating capacity, and hundreds of miles of levees and other flood protection structures. The plan gives navigation a priority subordinate to beneficial consumptive use functions, in cases involving water rising west of the 97th meridian. Provides that Corps reservoirs may include irrigation purpose in 17 western states.

Specifies that the Secretary of the Army shall prescribe regulations for the use of storage allocated for flood control or navigation to all reservoirs connected wholly or in part with federal funds. Authorizes providing facilities in reservoir areas for public use, including recreation and conservation of fish and wildlife. Includes a precedent-setting statement that Congress will adopt policy recognizing rights and interests of states in water resources development, and requiring consultation and coordination with affected states.

1945 Congress authorizes, in the Rivers and Harbors Act (P.L. 14, 79th Congress), nine-foot navigation channel on Missouri River downstream from Sioux City, Iowa.

1946 Corps begins work on Garrison Dam, and condemns land on Standing Rock and Rosebud Sioux Reservations needed for Fort Randall project in South Dakota.

1948 Congress authorizes a $5.1 million settlement with Three Affiliated Tribes of the Fort Berthold Reservation.

1950 Congress establishes guidelines for settlement negotiations with Cheyenne River and Standing Rock Sioux Tribes for the Oahe project.

1951 Catastrophic floods in lower Missouri basin produce discharges of 636,000 cubic feet per second at the river's confluence with the Mississippi. Nation records its first $1 billion flood.

1952 Flooding is extensive in the upper and middle Missouri basin. A discharge of 500,000 cubic feet per second is recorded at Bismarck, North Dakota, and the cities of Omaha, Nebraska, and Council Bluffs, Iowa are threatened.

1952 President Truman appoints the Missouri Basin Survey Commission to study basin development plan and administration. The Commission recommends creating a Missouri River Basin Commission, with some members dissenting.

1953 Garrison Dam closed. Missouri River Division creates Reservoir Control Center.

1955 Garrison Dam completed.

1957 Congress authorizes $12.3 million settlement with Standing Sioux Tribe for Oahe damages.

1958 The Water Supply Act permits the incorporation of storage space in Corps and BOR reservoirs for future domestic, municipal, and industrial water needs.

1958 U.S. District Court in North Dakota blocks Corps attempt to condemn land on Standing Rock Sioux Reservation for Oahe project.

1959 U.S. Senate Select Committee on National Water Resources recommends studies of water and related land resources are undertaken for all river basins in the nation. Recommendations are eventually translated into legislation in the Water Resources Planning Act of 1965.

1963 Formation of Missouri Basin Systems Group leads to organization of Basin Electric Power Corporative. U.S. Supreme Court reaffirms the Winters doctrine in Arizona v. California and clarifies the question of quantification of Indian reserved water rights.

1964 Congress directs that any Pick-Sloan Project not yet initiated would have to be "hereafter authorized" by Congress.

1965 Congress requires consideration in Federal Water Project Recreation Act of opportunities for outdoor recreation and fish and wildlife enhancement in planning water resources projects. Recreational use of the project is to be coordinated with other existing and planned federal, state, or local recreational developments.

1965 Congress reauthorizes Garrison Diversion Unit to serve 250,000 acres of irrigated land.

1967 First year main stem Missouri River dams operate as a system.

1968 Wild and Scenic Rivers Act requires that plans for water resource development consider setting aside certain streams as wild, scenic, or recreational rivers as an alternative to other uses. A portion of the upper Missouri in Montana is included in the Act.

1969 The National Environmental Protection Act (NEPA) commits the nation to responsibility for the quality of the environment. The Act requires an Environmental Impact Statement (EIS) on proposed federal actions affecting the environment.

1970 Congress passes River and Harbor and Flood Control Act stating objectives of enhancing regional economic development, the quality of the total environment, including its protection and improvement, the well-being of people, and the national economical development are to be included in federally financed water resource projects. Congress authorizes "Pick-Sloan Missouri Basin Program."

1972 The Missouri River Basin Commission (MRBC) is created by Presidential Executive Order 11658. The commission is principal coordinator of federal, state, interstate, local and nongovernmental entities for water and related land resource development in the basin.

1982 Congress makes clear in the Reclamation Reform Act that the provisions of federal reclamation law are not applicable to lands which receive benefits from water resources projects constructed by the Corps, except in limited circumstances.

1984 Garrison Diversion Unit Commission reduces Garrison project to 131,940 acres of new irrigation in North Dakota.

1986 Congress passes a the first comprehensive water resource bill in sixteen years. It states, "The Pick-Sloan Missouri Basin Program shall be prosecuted, as authorized and in accordance with applicable laws including the requirements for economic feasibility, to its ultimate development on an equitable basis as rapidly as may be practicable, within the limits of available funds and the cost recovery and repayment principals established by Senate Report No. 470 and House Report No. 282, 89th Congress, 1st session."

1987 U.S. Supreme Court agrees to hear appeals on the issue raised regarding authority of the Secretary of the Interior over water stored in the Missouri River main stem reservoirs, but declines to rule on the even larger issue of the federal and state governments' relative interests in Missouri River water.

1989 Protracted drought and shifting priorities in basin water use prompt Missouri Basin states and Corps to undertake review of the Master Water Control Manual for reservoir operations. Focus of review is a consideration of alternative scenarios for operating the river.

1990 Upper basin states of Montana, South Dakota, and North Dakota, concerned about impact on spawning fish, file suit at the U.S. District Court level arguing against use of drought-reduced water in the reservoirs for the benefit of downstream navigation. States claim the Corps was harming economic development in the region by causing damage to their recreation industries. The U.S Court of Appeals Eighth Circuit overrules a federal judge who ordered a reduction in the water releases from a reservoir in the Dakotas.

1991 Montana, South Dakota, and North Dakota file suit in U.S. District Court alleging the Corps violates the intent of the Flood Control Act of 1944 in operating the main stem reservoir system and requests the courts in to declare the rights of the states based on priorities for the basin that reflects contemporary uses and needs. Downstream states counter with amicus briefs showing major negative impacts if courts were to order Corps to redefine priorities.

1992 Missouri files suit in U.S. District Court to prohibit the Corps from reducing the level of flow in the Missouri River below the amount specified in the water control plan contained in the Missouri Manual.

1993 Missouri Basin States Association changes its name to the Missouri River Basin Association reflecting the association's expanded perspective and representation to include Indian Tribes.

1993 U.S. District Court dismisses suit filed by South Dakota, North Dakota, and Montana against Corps.

1997 Record moisture and snowfalls in the upper basin contribute to a 200-Year flood event in many areas. Total Missouri River runoff at Sioux City, Iowa is 49 Million Acre-Feet. Missouri River flooding is minor with dams successfully controlling flows. (Graph on page 4.)

2003 Dredging needed to open water intake for Heskett Station power plant on the Mandan side of the Missouri River near Bismarck. Other communities along the river face water supply problems, yet the Corps continues to drain the river down.

APPENDIX

1. River stage: The river stage levels referred to in this text are the Bismarck river gauge levels and are used to explain the river levels under different conditions. All river cities throughout the world have established their own river gauge to record their various river levels. My guess is that those who established the Bismarck gauge estimated "0" to be the level of the bottom of the river. A figure of 1,618.4 should be added to each Bismarck reading to convert it to the elevation above sea level.

2. High bottomland: Land that was built by the action of the river and is above a 13-foot river stage. There is no record of the June rise flooding high bottomland. (An exception would have been 1997 when a 200-year event would have flooded high bottomland if the Garrison Dam were not in place.)

3. Riparian: pertaining to the land along the banks of the river.

4. Rip-rap: protection of riparian land by placing stones on the riverbanks.

5. Alluvial: banks and bottoms of rivers composed of earth.

6. Aggradations: the building up or shallowing of a river by the deposition of silt. Example: the delta in Bismarck.

7. Degradation: the deepening of a river bottom by the removal of earth usually by the scouring action of flowing water. Example: the river immediately downstream from the Garrison Dam.

8. Missouri River between Fort Peck Dam, Montana, and Gavins Point Dam, South Dakota and Nebraska. Section 9 of the Act entitled "An Act authorizing the construction of certain public works on rivers and harbors for flood control, and for other purposes", approved December 22, 1944 (58 Stat. 891), is amended by adding at the end thereof the following new subsection:

"(f) The Secretary of the Army is directed to undertake such measures, including maintenance and rehabilitation of existing structures, which the Secretary determines are needed to alleviate bank erosion and related problems associated with reservoir releases along the Missouri River between Fort Peck Dam, South Dakota and Nebraska. The cost of such measures may not exceed $3,000,000 per fiscal year. Notwithstanding any other provisions of law, the costs of these measures, including the costs of necessary real estate interests and structural features, shall be apportioned among project purposes as a joint-use operation and maintenance expense. In lieu of structural measures, the Secretary may, if deemed appropriate, purchase affected land from willing sellers."

The above Section 33 was passed with the first $3 million appropriation due to the efforts of Senator Quentin Burdick and the BOMMM Board. However, the Corps decided (although it was not included in this law) that they would not protect land unless it had a favorable benefit-cost ratio and their BC study included only the depreciated value of the eroding land. We, including Senator Burdick, attempted to have them include loss of habitat, the effect of the downstream delta including increased spring and fall ice jams, reduction of winter power production, loss of dam storage capacity, loss of river channel capacity. But the Corps refused, obviously encouraged by the preservationists who wanted the river to remain "natural" and to prevent riverside development. Now Section 33 is going through an Environmental Impact Study by the Corps to determine the "adverse" effects of riprap. Guess what this EIS will report!

9. Missouri Basin Survey Commission Report of 1953 of the Souix City to St. Louis reach. On page 113 0f the Report states, "Of the total estimated benefits attributed to channel stabilization, 25 percent is credited to navigation and 75 percent to bank erosion control and land enhancement.

10. North Dakota state laws 47-06-05 Riparian Accretions. Where from natural causes land forms by imperceptible degrees upon the bank of a river or stream, navigable or not, either by accumulation of material, or by the recession of the stream, such land belongs to the owner of the bank, subject to any existing right of way over the bank.

11. 61-33-01 sovereign lands means those areas, including beds and islands, lying within the ordinary high water mark of navigable lakes and streams. Lands established to be riparian accretion or reliction lands pursuant to section 47-06-05 are considered to be above the high water mark and are not sovereign lands.

Andy Mork was raised on the Mork family farm located in Morton County in central North Dakota. His parents homesteaded in southern Morton County then moved to the Missouri River high bottomland north of Mandan in 1931.

In the pre-dam era prior to 1953, the Mork family knew the river as described by its nicknames "Old Muddy" and "Big Muddy". The river was a lot different then and so were the lives of the farmers who lived near it. Each spring they moved anything portable, mobile and valuable to high ground just in case the river got greedy. Ice jams and spring flooding were common and animals, equipment and buildings were often carried away.

The river offered little in terms of recreation. It was perilous to navigate and held primarily rough fish.

"Swimming in the Missouri was the equivalent of a mudbath with a current," Mork recalls.

Mork left the region after high school to pursue an education in the field of electrical engineering at the famous IBM Schools in New York City and Endicott, New York. The company's distinctive motto THINK was inscribed in stone over the Endicott school's main door. Thomas J. Watson, IBM chief executive and the school's founder also had his Five Steps to Knowledge "Read, Listen, Discuss, Observe, Think" carved into the Endicott school's front entrance, something Mork took to heart.

Following his training, Mork was employed with IBM in the eastern United States. When World War II began, all IBM facilities were placed at the disposal of the U.S. government. The war years also set IBM on the path of the computer industry, but Andy's future lay elsewhere.

In 1945, Mork returned to the Missouri River Valley and the family farm. Congress had passed the Flood Control Act just one year earlier and Mork became deeply interested in water issues and their impact on the residents of this semi-arid region. Raising corn, small grain, alfalfa and livestock, the family farm operation made use of the river for irrigation. With the impending completion of Garrison Dam, Mork foresaw the river's potential in terms of water quality, flood control, environmental, cultural, agricultural, industrial and recreational benefits.

Mork has served on the Morton County Water Resource Board since 1963. He served as State Water Resource Board President. He is currently the chairman of the Missouri West Water System, and of BOMMM (Burleigh, Oliver, Morton, Mercer, and McLean Counties) Joint Water Resource Board. He has been active as a soil conservation supervisor, state president of the Professional Soil Classifiers Board. He has also served on the State Soil Conservation Board and has served as a rural electric director and Basin Electric director.

In 2000, Mork was inducted into the North Dakota Water Users Hall of Fame. He is a frequent speaker at events pertaining to the Missouri River and water resource management.

Mork says that after all other analysis is complete, the practical test of water quality can be boiled down to one simple question: "But does it make a good cup of coffee?"

-Paula Crain Grosinger

View of Missouri River from Double Ditch historic site north of Bismarck. Mork farm is on opposite bank.

To order additional copies of

North Dakota's Missouri River

send check for $14.95

(includes sales tax, shipping and handling)

for each copy ordered to:

Crain Grosinger Publishing
P.O. Box 55
Mandan, ND 58554

To pay by credit card call:

701-663-0846; 877-566-2665 (toll-free)

Libraries and schools deduct $2.00 for each book ordered.

To schedule Andy Mork as a speaker call:

701-663-3840

82